how to found your own religion

and other stories

how to found your own religion

and other stories

by Francis J. Phelan, C. S. C.

illustrations by Robert E. Rambusch

HELICON *Baltimore • Dublin*

Helicon Press, Inc.
1120 N. Calvert Street
Baltimore 2, Maryland

Helicon Limited
53 Capel Street
Dublin, Ireland

Library of Congress Catalog Card Number: 63–12096

First Edition

"And the Devil a Monk Was He" originally appeared in the April, 1958 issue of *The Catholic World* and is reprinted here with their kind permission.

PRINTED IN THE UNITED STATES OF AMERICA
BY GARAMOND PRESS, BALTIMORE, MARYLAND

contents

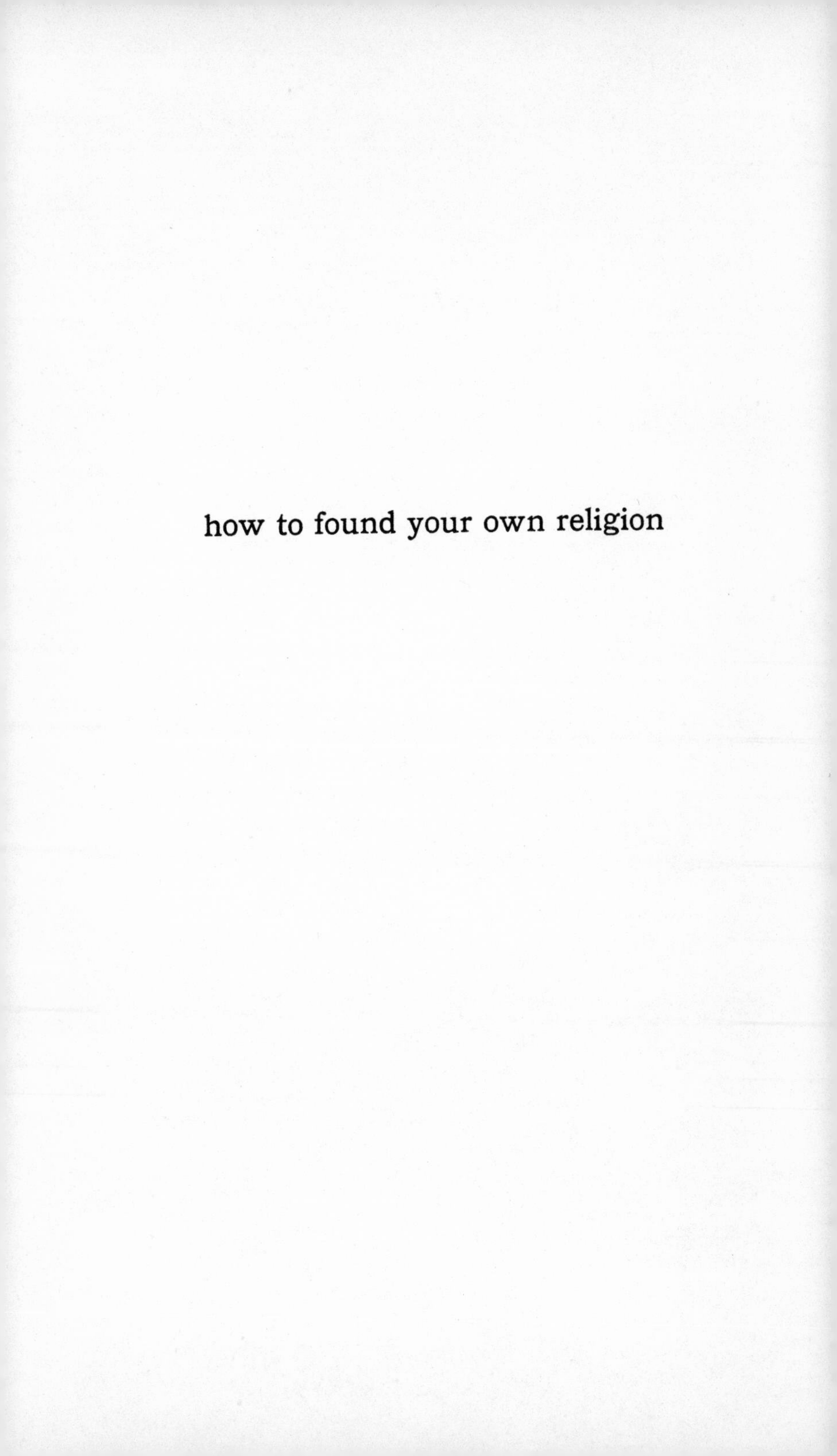

how to found your own religion

not by pills alone

Now it came to pass in those days that Man progressed from strength to strength, first discovering America, then learning to fly, and yet later reaching out to investigate the secrets of space. But perhaps none of these accomplishments compared with his development of the Happiness Pill.

These pills were called by different names, some stressing their tranquillizing value, others bringing out the warm feeling of benevolence that the pills brought to their users. Many people readily came to appreciate their value, and depended upon the pills to tide them over the bad spots in life.

But no one appreciated them more than Lucifer, for his great mind saw that here was a blessing that could easily be turned into a curse.

"Shades of the Garden of Eden," he said to himself. "Man is always partaking of something that will solve everything. Now, behold, he has found Happiness, locked up in the heart of a pill."

The Devil reasoned that, if Man was going to live by pills, he, Lucifer, was certainly not going to be caught behind the times. "Soon there will be not only Happiness Pills," he said, "but Lust, Anger, Gluttony, Envy and Sloth pills, if I have anything to do with it."

He had quite a bit to do with it. Not long after, he

had all Hell working night and day, producing every conceivable type of pill. They had catchy trade names: Sanomort, Reprobon, Contaminil, Lechotabs and Depravoplex (which was also known as K70).

The Devil's effort came along at just the right time. Everybody was taking so many happiness pills that they were happy all the time, even when things were going wrong and they knew they should be sad. They didn't want to give up happiness, but they did want to have a brief period of anger or sorrow at the right times, for no one wants to appear completely inhuman at the death of a friend, or at the scene of an accident.

The Devil's signs went up everywhere: "Mother-in-Law die?" one read, "—Have a Grief Pill. You'll feel worse faster."

Of course the Devil was not the only one to get into the business. As soon as his pills were seen to be moving fast, other manufacturers produced them too, and the advertising took on a new competitive slant: "3 Times Faster," said one company of its Anger Pill. "Clinical Tests prove that our pills make you mad 3 times as fast as other leading brands. *And*—they make you 3 times as angry!"

But Anger Pills weren't the only ones. There was soon demand for other kinds to meet other kinds of problems.

Certain people, for instance, for some not-too-clear reason, felt the need to feel jealous. Manufacturers were surprised that people actually enjoyed jealousy, or at least wanted to feel jealous, but nevertheless they were quick to fill the demand.

There were other surprises, too, as when a man wrote in to one company:

Dear Sirs:

Why is it that you have no pill for Sloth? Everywhere I look about me I see people taking pills only to bring on frenetic activity. Nowhere, however, do I find a pill that will turn me into the kind of creature I want to be—a lazy, good-for-nothing parasite, who spends all his time between bed and the ice box. Please develop such a pill fast, and in the meantime send me some more of your regular Gluttony ones, which are the best you seem to be able to do at the present time.

Thank you in advance.

An idea of how the Anger Pills worked can be gotten from the case of a man named George. He was a quiet little man, very well respected at the office for his work, but hen-pecked at home and something of a doormat to the rest of his family. He was too gentle and too patient to get mad at anything, and his family constantly ignored his wishes because of this. For example they would take the paper out of George's hands as he was reading it every evening, saying that there was something they wanted to see for just a minute. Of course, then they never gave it back, and this bothered George.

One day he said to himself, "If only I could get angry at the proper times, then maybe my family would listen to me." So he got some Anger Pills.

The next time his wife tried the newspaper trick, George reached into his watch pocket for an Anger Pill, and flipped it into his mouth. As it was a very fast-acting brand of pill, George immediately became ferociously angry. He jumped up and down, his eyes bulged, and the veins stood out in his neck. He crouched down like a Great Ape, and he pounded the floor with his fists. Then he grabbed a very heavy ash tray stand and swung it around in the air above his head, telling his wife that if she did not give him back his newspaper he would kill her with his ash tray. George did not have much trouble after that with people stealing his newspapers. In fact he soon became impossible to live with, and his wife got a divorce, taking the children with her.

A case that turned out much differently was that of Alexander, the real estate man. Such were the ups and downs of his trade that Alexander had long been given to the use of Happiness Pills to take him through life. He eventually became dependent upon the pills and was as a result nearly always slightly happy. In fact he was so continually happy that it was ruining his business. People would try to pull deals on him, and he would see what they were trying to do and know that he should become mad and stop them. They would draw up contracts that had him paying them to take his own property away from him. Or, hoping to catch him in a gay mood, they would call up and ask him if he would please tear up the mortgage for them now. Quite frequently when he sold especially valuable pieces of property he was so elated over the deal that he would take no money. And as he nearly always had a Happiness Pill in him, he found that he could not get angry at the right times. Alas, however, neither could he give up his Happiness Pills.

When the new Anger Pill came out, it was the perfect solution to Alexander's problem. From then on, when someone tried to cheat him he would turn away and quickly flip into his mouth an Anger Pill. Then he would fly into a rage, and pounce upon the people who were trying to cheat him. Of course Alexander lost clients this way, but at least he was not cheated so often.

However, much later when the other new types of pills came out, Alexander was a natural for them, too, for the Happiness Pills kept him in such a constant state of contentment that he was in sore need of almost all the other emotional reactions.

It was a nuisance for example to go to a movie that was a thriller or perhaps a great tragedy, and not be able to experience any feeling of shock or fear, simply because he had just had a Happiness Pill. So Alexander bought all kinds of pills, and when he was going to a movie that he knew was going to be sad, he took a Sadness Pill, and so felt very sad during the movie; or if it was a horror movie he would take a Fear Pill and go almost out of his mind with fright.

But Alexander got into the bad habit of carrying all his pills with him everywhere he went, each kind in a different pocket of his vest. Generally he was careful about which pocket he reached into, but one day at the office when Alexander was feeling happy, as usual, from his Happiness Pills, a client tried to pull on him one of the worst deals he'd ever heard of—Alexander knew it would ruin him if he let it go through. So quickly he reached for his Anger Pills, and prepared to let the man have it. But in the pressure of the moment, Alexander forgot which pocket he kept his Anger Pills in, and instead of one of them his hand drew out a Sloth Pill. The man kept talking about the preposterous deal, and Alexander kept growing more and more tired. Finally he said, "Look, Henry, (for that was the client's name) I'm beat, I really am. I'm going to sack for a while on the divan. You just draw the thing up and I'll sign it." So while Alexander snored, the client prepared the awful contract, and Alexander woke up only long enough to sign his business away.

That was the last anyone heard from Alexander, until his obituary appeared two months later in the newspaper. It said that he had died "from an overdose of Hope Pills."

Mothers caught on very quickly to the use of pills to quiet their children. It became customary that whenever a baby would start to cry, someone would shove tranquillizer pills down its throat until it stopped.

Then, with good reason, mothers became worried as the children grew up without any normal human reaction except continual happiness, which is not normal, and so they started using the other new pills to supply their offspring with normal reactions. They gave their children pills to throw tantrums with, pills to start to school with, and pills to keep them going.

Of course some people resisted the pill craze, but in a lot of places everyone became an addict. In these sections, when the new pill generation reached maturity they were a very odd set indeed. Everything about them seemed strangely artificial. Most of the time, it is true, they were able to remember which occasion demanded which emotion, but after they got a little older some of them began forgetting this, and it became clear what had happened: the unfortunate members of the Pill Generation had never experienced any emotions naturally—everything had been done artificially. They grew up learning to react according to the pill that was popped into their mouth. Then as

ENVY
SAD
FEAR
LUST
GLAD
HOPE
MAD

they grew older and were taught how to use pills themselves, it required a very great effort for them to memorize which situations demanded which emotions. They were well trained, and their memories doubtless performed prodigious feats in remembering the complicated combinations for every foreseeable situation, but as they grew older you could see some of them giving up, and getting careless, and more and more they reacted wrongly, so that it got so bad that no one was shocked at any reaction a member of the Pill Generation made to anything.

Music meant nothing to them, or else it called forth all the wrong responses. The more conscientious of them would feel obliged to show *some* mark of appreciating good music, but generally these responses were just the opposite of what they should have been. When Beethoven's 9th would be played, you could notice them glancing around at others, to see whether this was a thing to dance to or whistle to. Similarly at a performance of Hamlet you had to get used to untimely laughter, bursts of applause at the wrong times, and so on.

The creative artists were hard hit. Playwrights, after going through the agony of consuming the proper amount of pills to produce a play, were justifiably annoyed whenever they found critics too lazy to keep up on *their* pills. But the critics, understandably enough, replied that they were critics, not physicians.

Perhaps it was hardest of all on the poets. In order to read a poem you had to know with what pill it had been written, and so the poets had to discreetly supply the information along with their lines. People complained that reading poetry was getting too much like having a prescription filled, and indeed, many a poet wondered why he had not gone into pharmacy instead.

And so it was that in those places where the pills had taken over culture and civilization progressively deteriorated as more and more of the Pill Generations appeared, until finally only a few very old people were left to tell what emotions went with what stimuli. Then even these old people died, and no one knew how to feel about anything, and the Age of Tranquillity descended over the earth, until it could be said in all truth that Man was indeed at peace with himself, more so in fact than the very vegetables of the field.

and the devil a monk was he

One day the Devil realized with irritation that he had been completely neglecting those great citadels of Catholicism, the religious houses. He was especially angry with himself because even the most poorly informed person knows that the Devil takes very special care of a monastery. There are, as we know, even more devils hovering around monasteries than there are around dens of iniquity.

At once he started looking through vocational literature and consulting the vocation ads in the Catholic magazines. "We take anybody," said one advertisement, and the Devil chuckled to himself, wondering how happy they would be to take him if they knew who he was. He had another good laugh over one entitled "Belated Vocations," because he was well aware that his own "vocation" was unquestionably the most belated of all time. A few of the appeals made him sick, so enthusiastic were they over things like prayer and charity.

Finally he came across exactly what he wanted: one of the old and revered orders that was just semi-cloistered enough to get in trouble. He could tell by the apologetic tone of their advertisement how anxious they were to be thought modern and up with the times.

His application was quickly accepted, and soon there

he was with the other monks, looking a great deal holier than the best of them. He took the name of Nefarious, and it was not long before Brother Nefarious was known as a very good rule-keeper; in fact he eventually became the Abbot's trusted right-hand man, advising him on all those difficult decisions that must be faced by ancient monasteries which try to keep pace with modern times.

For a long time he fought all innovations, acting hurt at each relaxation the Abbot introduced, until the other council members would correct him, saying, "Brother Nefarious, you are too strict! You will have to learn to temper this zeal of thine, and learn to compromise, for the good of the monastery." But he would only shrug a little, as if he disapproved of such goings-on.

So he bided his time, until one day the question came up, as it was bound to, about what to do with television.

The Abbot and all the other monks on the council were firmly opposed to it in any form. But by this time, so great was the odor of sanctity about Brother Nefarious that all quickly gave ear when he broke his long-standing strictness to recommend humbly that the monastery invest in a good, large TV-set. As a matter of fact, he became for a few moments rather vehement as he denounced anyone who would think of depriving the monks who labored all day of such an honest, wholesome and cultural experience as TV. So great was his ardor on this occasion that some said you could actually smell the fire and brimstone as he spoke.

So they bought the set; unfortunately, however, those who designed the monastery (it was a direct copy of one built in the eleventh century) had left no provision for such a thing as a television room. Clearly, the set would have to be placed in some room already used for another purpose.

Now one of the proudest possessions of the old monastery was its library, or Scriptorium as it was called. Next to the chapel itself, the library was the very center of the life of the monks. It was a long, narrow room with stacks of priceless books and scrolls lining the walls, and a bit dark, so that it was ideal for watching television. There would be no harm, the Abbot reasoned, in using the room for this double purpose, since the television was obviously only going to be on for an hour after the evening meal, a time when no monk ought to be browsing anyway.

For a while this worked out very nicely. Then the monks noticed a religious program that came on directly after the usual TV hour, and permission was granted for that, along with several other very spiritual attractions. And the first World Series they had it for fairly clamored to be watched, as did two fine variety shows which were put on the approved list, one for Saturday night and one for Sunday.

Somewhere during the second year of the set's presence, the better monks began to notice that the thing seemed to be on pretty nearly all the time. But it was very legitimate, for if you asked the monks who were watching, they always had permission, and when you got tired working out on the long rows of cabbage and the even longer rows of beans, and asked why certain brothers were not out helping, someone usually said, "They have permission to watch a certain TV show in which they are interested."

Soon it got so that all afternoon, it seemed, and every afternoon, there was a handful of brothers watching the baseball game. They were not wearing their habits for it was hot in the room, and they were always shouting about "the Sox" and "the Yankees."

The ones who noticed this most of all were of course the brothers whose duty it was to work with the manuscripts, copying them and doing research. Whenever you came into the library to find a book, the baseball brothers would shout at you for standing in the way. It was very dark, and if you had to ask one of them to move, the rest would all ask you who you were trying to impress. Some of the bolder librarian monks tried to turn the lights up to find their books, but this was met by enraged shouts of blasphemy. Some of these shouts came from the baseball brothers, but the most violent ones (though no one stopped to notice) always came from Brother Nefarious, sitting there in the darkness. He was a great Yankee fan.

Soon this conflict became a real problem for the monastery. The ones in charge of the library went to the Abbot and presented their case. They said that not only were those watching afternoon and morning TV a great distraction to the library monks, but that, in fact, it often happened that those who went into the library to search for a book did not come back; others could not seem to remember why they went and, though it was a sorry thing to have to admit, some library brothers made the excuse of having to get a book, merely so they could watch TV. Things finally got so bad that when anyone said he had to "go get a book" everyone knew he meant that he was going to watch television.

The Abbot saw wisdom in their complaint, but he felt that it was also true that a custom had developed which, though not yet having the force of law, should not be disturbed, as respect for custom is so important to the religious life. He said, "Let us speak with Brother Nefarious about this. He will have the answer."

So they called in Brother Nefarious, who said, "Certainly; it is something I have been wishing to bring up myself. It is not a simple problem—it is one which demands a very bold solution.

"Fortunately, as you intimate, I have a solution, but I fear that you will think it too bold, and so I feel very reluctant to mention it."

When they heard that he had a solution, everyone pressed him not to refrain from sharing it with them. He protested again and again, saying that it was too novel, requiring too much fortitude for the average monk to see in it the only honest and workable way.

At this the Abbot sat there wringing his hands, for he could see the spiritual peace of his monastery being threatened by this obstinate monk who had the answer but would not share it. He commanded Brother Nefarious with all the authority he could invoke to tell them exactly what the plan was, "without watering it down in any way."

"Well," said Brother Nefarious, "the TV set obviously must be removed from the library (at this a gasp went up from the habitual television watchers) and since there is no other common room to put it in, why then I can see no other way to continue this great blessing but to arrange for each monk to pursue the goals of culture in private."

"You mean, place a few sets in some of the private rooms?" the old Abbot asked cautiously.

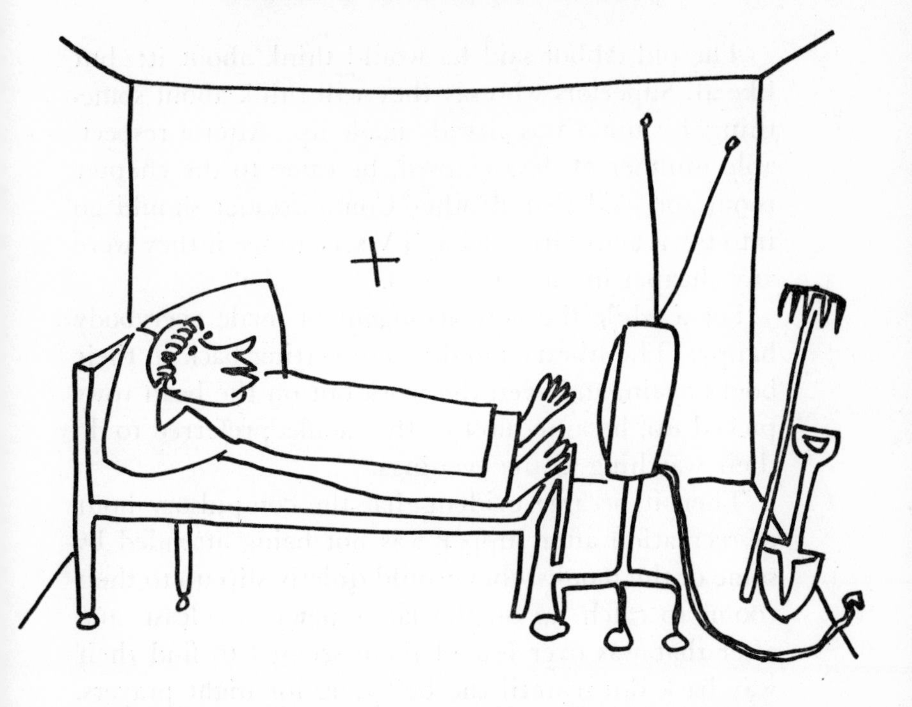

"In *every* private room. That which is true in the greater is also true in the less. In this day and age, modern, convenient, and relatively economic TV is available in the form of portable sets. Each cell could possess one without any crowding whatever. They can be stored neatly back of the prie-dieu when not in use."

There was a long pause at this. "I see now what you meant, Brother Nefarious, when you said that this plan requires great fortitude. It is indeed novel," said the old Abbot pensively.

"True," said the Angel of Darkness, "but like all courageous acts, it possesses great and immediate advantages. When this place gets TV in every room, who will ever think of it as a traditional monastery, out of contact with the present? I can just see our vocational ads: 'A 21-inch TV set in every room.' "

The old Abbot said he would think about it: but like all Superiors who say they will think about something, his mind was already made up. After a respectable number of days elapsed, he came to the chapter room and said that Brother Commissioner should go into town and start pricing TV sets, to see if they were any cheaper in large numbers.

For a while the new arrangement made everybody happy. The library monks were getting back to their books again, and even the work out on the bean rows picked up, because most of the monks preferred to do their watching in the evenings.

Then it became evident that the compulsory hour of recreation after supper was not being attended by some of the monks; they would quietly slip up to their rooms to catch up on the latest news broadcast, and after that was over few of them seemed to find their way back down until the bell rang for night prayers. And in fact, to the more astute observer it became noticeable that several of the brothers were not even making it to that. Nothing was said about it, however, perhaps because the old Abbot himself was not making it to night prayers very often, either. On the occasions when he was not present, Brother Nefarious gracefully accepted the role of preserver of monastic discipline, and led prayers in clear, bell-like tones. He never missed exercises, because it was essential to his purposes that he keep an irreproachable reputation. And he also was toying with the idea of being the next Abbot.

And so, imperceptibly but steadily the spiritual life of the monks deteriorated. They couldn't get up in the morning because they stayed up so late in the evening, watching the late late show. They couldn't meditate, because their rule commanded that this be done in the privacy of one's own cell, and very scarce was the monk who could go there without fumbling with the TV switch. Most of them had their sets hooked up so that when they turned on the light, the TV went on, and was on for as long as they were in the room. They were somehow able to get their spiritual reading in, one eye on the book and one eye on knife-throwing acts, chorus lines, wrestling, or whatever happened to be on.

Along about this time, someone casually remarked that the reception was not what it should be. At this, Brother Nefarious swung into action. What was needed, he said, was a really big antenna. Next day he could be seen high atop the monastery spire, removing the cross, and replacing it with a huge, rotating antenna.

"I've been wanting to do this for some time," he said. "No one looks at this very much around here any way," he added, tossing the cross to the ground. "The antenna is shaped just like it, and no one will ever notice."

The monk helping him agreed, and laughingly said, "Only God will know the difference."

Up to this time, whatever else might be said about the programs the brothers watched, at least it must be admitted that they were normal broadcast television. Now, however, the Devil decided that the time had come to stop treating the monks like children; he was tired of keeping within natural means—the time had come to use some of the vast supernatural forces at his disposal.

Soon the brothers were watching programs seen by no other viewers in the country. It would have surprised them mightily had they compared their reception with their neighbors'; it had certain phenomenal qualities about it, as did the subject matter. The Devil laughingly said to himself that it was time "to raise a little hell," and that is exactly what he did. He raised whole sections of it up to earth, packaging it neatly and inserting it within the time limits of the brothers' favorite programs. So cleverly was it done that while the commercials remained the same, everything else was all Lucifer's. Each one of the masterpieces could have borne the credit "Made In Hell" on it very legitimately, for Lucifer was producer, director, and the leading actor in every one of them.

All were within the limits of good taste, of course. Even shows with such titles as "Love and Lust" were not what is commonly termed "offensive" and anyway, the brothers were no prudes. The shows were instead very subtle and charming, and could be seen by any broadminded religious seeking culture. But they were deadly, all the same.

In the end it was the choir obligation that caused all the trouble. You must know that all the great monasteries sing praises to the Lord seven times a day; they recite the entire psalter in doing so, and it is in this beautiful prayer that they find much of their reason for existence. Everything about the monastery leads only to this; and everything that the Devil does about a monastery is aimed ultimately against the worship of God, which he finds extremely distasteful.

For this reason, the Devil knew that he must do what is usually termed "precipitating a crisis." For by everything he had so far done he still had not succeeded in making the monks break their choir obligation. Somehow he had to make this obligation clash more violently with the deeply in-built addiction the monks now had to television.

So he conceived the idea of whipping up an especially "spiritual" program that began just a few minutes before the monks finished Vespers. In order to see much of the program, therefore, the monks had to hurry through Divine Office. However, the Devil, since he was not only producer but also station manager of this particular closed TV circuit, slowly moved back the starting time of the program. The more time the monks gained by rushing through office, the more time they found they had lost, because the program always seemed to be starting earlier. Finally someone had the idea (no one noticed who it was, but it was probably Brother Nefarious) that they would all save fully five minutes if, instead of racing to their cells to see the program, they had a set placed, with all propriety, in the back of the chapel, all tuned up and ready to go at the end of the *Salve Regina*.

They did this, and every day as the monks slammed their books shut, Brother Nefarious would turn up the volume and they would happily watch what was, after all, a very learned spiritual lecture, coming as it did from the immensely wise intellect of a fallen angel.

The Abbot would not have approved of thus using the chapel, but for many months now, he had accepted the privilege of rank and skipped office in common, to watch the program in his room.

Then one day the Devil made his final assault. He pretended that something was wrong with the light socket in the back of the chapel, and picked up the set to move it to the front of the chapel. Everything happened very quickly, so that for an instant, the TV set was enthroned in the front of the chapel, while the monks were still on their knees, just finishing up the office. This at any rate was what the photographers caught who had just entered the chapel, tracking down rumors of the strange things that had been going on at the monastery.

It was also the picture that was on the front pages of many papers across the country next day. "MONKS WORSHIP TELEVISION IN BACKWARD AREA," said one headline. "WEIRD RITES, MODERN VOODOO" screamed another. "SECRET CULT OF ELECTRONIC MARVELS" shouted a third. And in the picture sections there were many photographs showing the monks having a good time watching television in their cells while the weeds grew high among the corn and bean rows.

Today there is not much left of the old place. As you drive by, you can see that the fields have turned to stubble, and there are patches of blue sky showing through the old vaulted ceiling of the chapel, where once the Divine Office was chanted.

And some people say that if you look closely, you can still make out on the roof a rusted and twisted television antenna, moaning and howling in the wind.

the baptism of jazz

Some years ago in a city in the eastern part of the United States there used to be a church that was called the Church of the Broad Progression. This name puzzled many people, and taxi drivers used to tell their passengers that it was named after one of the mysteries of the New Testament, like the Ascension. But it was not; it was called that simply because it was an extremely progressive church, and broadminded on all subjects.

One of the subjects its young minister, the Rev. Henderson, was most broadminded about was music. "Jazz is the only authentic American folk music," the likable and enthusiastic young man would say, "and unless we recognize this fact, we will never have any genuine church music in this country." On Sunday mornings after services he would talk to little groups of people on the church steps and say, "Jazz is the music of the people, and since this is the people's church, I intend to bring Jazz into the services if it's the last thing I do."

Quite a few of the hi-fi enthusiasts in the congregation supported him in this view. However, he knew that certain strong cross-sections of the parish were very much opposed to it.

One Sunday morning as he was standing by the church door just after finishing up his little talk with the usual "if it's the last thing I do," several members of the Ladies Auxiliary took him to task quite strongly.

"I wouldn't over-emphasize that last part if I were you, Reverend," said the club secretary.

And the club president at her side firmly added, "Young man, if your mother, Lord rest her, could hear you talking like that, she'd *turn* in her grave. When you were little, she'd have put soap in your mouth for saying a thing like that . . ."

The President of the Ladies Auxiliary would doubtless have gone on to give more details about the days of his youth, but at this moment one of the men in the group pressed forward and said, "Of course, Madam, maybe we're getting a little excited about something that doesn't exist—maybe we're all talking about two different things." It was the parish organist talking, an individual who knew his music so well that everyone had taken to calling him "The Music Man." It is only fair to add here that he was wearing a pin-striped suit, a trifle out of taste. Turning to the indignant ladies, he continued, "I'm sure Reverend Henderson when he speaks of Jazz is not speaking of the raucous, vulgar music you perhaps remember from the twenties." (He leered a bit, the ladies thought, as he said this.) "He's using the term, I feel quite sure, in a very definite technical sense, the way you might hear it used at Tanglewood or even Juillard—those of us in the profession know that the sort of music he's talking about is deeply spiritual; the fact is that it actually took up where the old Gregorian Chant of the Middle Ages left off. Jazz in this sense, far from being worldly or irreligious, begins to approach the hidden world of Mysticism. Indeed, it is often a small, short step that actually separates the true Jazz artist from the saint."

The women were obviously impressed by this unsuspected connection that Jazz had with religion, and were much relieved to hear that whatever it was that the young minister was going to bring in, it was at least respectably traditional, if not downright Medieval, in fact. The ladies had other worrying to do, about decorations and so on, and soon hurried off to attend to it.

"Thanks, Daddi-o," said the young minister as they moved off, for he liked to affect the language of the Beat Generation. "That was a real bad scene until you started to blow. But all kidding aside, where did you dig up that stuff about the plainchant—that's interesting."

"Glad you liked it," smiled the Music Man. "It's something I really had to work to come up with. In fact," he said, leaning closer, "it's a gem of an idea, and I think if we exploit it fully it can be made to bring Jazz into our church. Come on up to the choir loft and I'll show you what I mean."

Upstairs, it was plain that the organist had been working very hard. Stacks of old manuscripts showed that he had actually been going back to the ancient originals in order to get a deep understanding of the difficult business of plainchant notation.

"This is tough stuff," he said, and brought out some of the sheets with their odd-looking little square notes. "These notes are called *Neums.* This mark is called a *Quilisma,* and that thing over there is a *Pressus.* They called this one down here a *Torculus Strophicus,* whatever that is—I haven't been able to figure it out yet. This one is an *Episema.* If you keep looking at them long enough you begin to think you have spots before your eyes; and the funny part of it is, you have, and it's awfully hard to tell one spot from another."

After a few days more of heavy work, the organist came over to the rectory and announced that he thought he'd finally gotten the thing down. He said that now he felt that, by stretching a *Quilisma* here and there, and by adding an *Episema* at the right places, he could put any modern piece into the ancient and respectable notation.

He told the minister to examine closely a sheet of music he was carrying. "See anything there?" he asked.

The cleric did, and tried to hum the melody of whatever the piece was supposed to be. But he couldn't make anything out, and after a few tries, gave up. "What's it supposed to be?" he asked, puzzled.

"The Saint Louis Blues!" cried the Music Man, unable to hold the glee out of his voice. "I did it for practice. But it's a neat job, I must admit. Even a monk wouldn't be able to see anything there but the neums themselves; a very felicitous wedding, I feel, of the sacred and the profane."

Both were overjoyed, and by Sunday the clever organist had re-done enough Jazz into the new notation that he was able to give a whole service composed of strictly nothing but what he called "Gone Gregorian."

This splendid performance silenced much of the opposition, with the exception of a few centers of resistance such as the Ladies Auxiliary, which still was not convinced. "Bunch of squares," murmured the Music Man. Far from giving up, however, the ladies renewed the battle with so much ardor that once again

the minister felt that it might be advisable to call the whole thing off, and to content himself with a "square" parish, the way so many of his clerical friends had done. After all, he reasoned, even if he did manage to make his people see the light, there still would be the tremendous job of convincing the officials of the Synod. They were conservative men, the board members, and might take drastic steps before he had a chance to explain.

The Music Man was greatly distressed to hear him say that he was thinking of giving up, just when it seemed that victory was in their grasp. He kept trying to think of some additional tactic that would rescue them, but nothing came. However, he did manage to get the minister to promise that there would be no final decision until all possibilities had been explored.

The Music Man used to do his thinking at the organ. A conscientious musician, he used to spend hours playing every day. However, he looked much less like an organist at these times than like a honky-tonk piano player. Even though he was in church, a cigarette would invariably be dangling from his lips, his tie would be loose and his collar opened, and on some passages, his eyes seemed to be continually rolling backward to look up through the top of his head. At one moment he would lean down very close to the keyboard, and then again he would stretch so far back that he appeared to be in extreme danger of falling backward over the choir-loft railing to his doom on the church floor below.

This was the way he used to like to talk with the pastor about their project; he said he got many of his ideas for "the movement" this way. And the pastor really enjoyed coming over and listening to him, as he was indeed a fine musician. They used to have many a long chat. The Music Man accompanied everything he said with appropriate background music—chords, or peals of notes, were nicely fitted to each word. Or sometimes he would play extravagantly for a while, stop suddenly to make a remark, and then bang out a church-shattering blast. He had to watch out, though, that he didn't become carried away at times like these, for often when he was enjoying himself so much he would forget all about maintaining his identity as the Music Man, and would be violently brought back to reality when his cloven hoofs got caught in the foot pedals. This wasn't so bad when he was alone, but if the pastor was there the Devil quickly had to return to character, and hope that nothing had been noticed. Fortunately, the pastor was always so preoccupied with the movement that he never saw anything.

One day after an exceptionally bad slip, the Devil was wondering whether he had been found out, and the pastor suddenly looked him straight in the eye and said, "You're the devil of an organist; what do you think of Eurythmics?"

The Devil, intensely relieved, ran his thumb all the way up the keyboard, came back to hit one bass note, and said, "You mean (chords) Liturgical Dancing? (more chords) I'm all for it." Then he was back to his chords again.

"Glad to hear it. A lot of people laugh at it, but so many authorities say it's good stuff that I'd like to introduce it here."

This was met by no comment by the organist, just a little noncommittal fugue on the upper keyboard.

Then, however, the pastor said, "Gee, I'd love to hook up my Liturgical Dancing idea with your Gone Gregorian. They're made for each other."

At this the Music Man's mouth popped open, the cigarette fell from his lips, his eyes rolled backward, and the church was filled with a wild and majestic creation that signified Joy, Glory and Triumph. The organist was singing to it, and even screaming, but he was drowned out by the sound of his organ's mighty music. It was quite a while before the noise died down to where the minister could make out what the organist was saying. He was repeating over and over things like, "That's it" and "We've got it" and "We're in!"

The pastor agreed, and now the movement could go full speed ahead, for it was rather certain that no one, not even the Ladies Auxiliary, was going to oppose such a fine thing as Liturgical Dancing.

The first thing that was needed was an orchestra. The Music Man said he knew just what they wanted. He went off to hell, and there he got seven other devils more wicked than himself, and brought them back with him to play for the parish. "They're a very smooth combo," he said. "They just don't come any smoother."

When people inquired of them who they were, they said that they were known as the Legion Brothers. "There are a lot of us around," they would add, but that is just about the only comment they would make. However, they turned out to be a very fast crowd indeed, and were in quite a bit of mischief before they got around to playing for evening devotions. Their advertising slogan was "Music Out of This World," and more than one parishioner spoke more truly than he knew when he made some such remark as "That's a wicked trumpet player they've got there!"

Under the gentle nudging of the Music Man, the parish went through various stages of advance. At first, the affairs were hymn-sings rather than dances. At the very beginning the hymns were based on Hill-billy tunes, as these were so clearly folk music. Then several weeks later there was a period when they were all Western melodies. The people knew these tunes as well as the others, and were able to sing them out, loud and clear, even without looking at the Gregorian notation they had thoughtfully been provided with. It really doesn't take too much cleverness to sing *any* hymn to a tune like "Home, Home on the Range." No one even needs Gregorian notes for that.

Then they pushed the pews back, and the liturgical dancing started. A line from a psalm would be sung, and the dancers would interpret what the passage meant to them. It was really quite inspiring, and genuinely good art, where every movement and every gesture contributed a spiritual significance, just as in so many of the religious dances of the Orient.

The dancers were gradually working their way down through the books of the Bible, doing a fine job of interpreting it to the music, when one night just as they got to the Book of Proverbs someone introduced a little waltz beat into things. That was the end of the Bible, because the band went on to the Fox Trot and then the Charleston and the old people had to start pulling out of the services. They were a little bit irritated. They had gone to church faithfully for years, they said, and they were willing to see a few changes now and then, but this was carrying participation too far.

However, the young people of the parish took to it enthusiastically, and the pastor observed that, whatever else might be said against it, the new service certainly kept the youngsters off the streets.

After a while, the new mode of worship replaced more and more of the functions of the old. The pews were got rid of entirely. Neon lights blinked on and off outside, and the organist traded in the organ for an old piano. When he wasn't playing on this, or when the orchestra was silent, there were plenty of juke boxes available, all loaded with hit hymns.

In order to get a head start on Sunday morning services, these began late Saturday night, continuing until dawn. The Music Man said that this was as it should be ("Form should follow function" was the way he put it), and that it didn't worry him a bit: "I frankly don't care if we never go back to the old stuff again," he said. "Look at the crowds we're getting. You can't tell me we'd be making converts like this with the old routine." Then he shuffled off, beating on an imaginary drum, to help some new converts who wanted to know where the party was.

Eventually the Music Man decided that the time had come to give the people what they had been asking for right along, namely some really liturgical Rock and Roll. That evening started out rather calmly, with a soprano singing something from Gounod, but for the second number the Music Man modestly announced that they would all have the pleasure of dancing to a new composition of his, the *Church-House Rock*. This was met by excited screams, which continued on more or less for the remainder of the evening.

The little church was really jumping by the third

dance, and by the fourth, the building itself seemed to be rocking and rolling. By the seventh it was tugging at its foundations, and it was somewhere along about the tenth or eleventh that the little church tore itself loose and flew off into the night, according to men standing in the doorway of a saloon across the street. Of course, since the witnesses had been drinking, it is difficult to be quite certain exactly when it happened.

No one knows where it went, and nobody seems to care. One of the new interstate highways was built right through the middle of that area and the people of the neighborhood had other things to think about. They all had to move, too, and needless to say, some of them were very angry at the government.

charity comes to gerasa

Now in those days the Catholic diocese of Gerasa was having its problems. Some people thought that the biggest problem was the Bishop. He was a saint, but everyone said that the old man was slowing up; that he had let things come to a sorry pass, and that it wouldn't hurt the diocese one bit if a few changes were made in the way certain things were handled, both around the chancery and out in the parishes, too. Some went so far as to say that, as a matter of fact, all things considered, it would not even be such a bad idea if Gerasa got a new bishop.

Understandably, one of the Bishop's most outspoken critics was the Chancellor. It was his job to set straight all those things the old man kept forgetting about. For example, he had to spend long hours trying to piece together the episcopal schedule, because the Bishop was all the time letting things like visits from old women, informal chats, or anything at all hold him back from what the Chancellor called "this pressing business of running a diocese." It was not simply that the Chancellor was a young, efficient man, nor even that he was slated to succeed to the episcopacy. It was just that he knew better.

The old prelate had a long list of poor friends who knew exactly when he could be reached. Some of them were from Ireland, near where he was brought up himself. Others came to know him through the years when he was a pastor going out on sick calls, or straightening out family problems. The office people around the chancery called this group "The Bishop's Beggars" somewhat sarcastically, but also somewhat devotedly for the old folks had been around for so long that everyone regarded them as friends.

One of these was an ancient woman in a black shawl who was the first into the Cathedral in the morning and the last to be removed at night. She was present at every Mass, and every function, sitting in the first row on the Gospel side. She had an atrocious singing voice and sang very loud; she also prayed out loud at the wrong times, saying her own prayers no matter what the congregation was doing.

But the Bishop loved her for her piety, and used to feel very good when he could look down from the sanctuary and see her there. And on those few mornings when she missed, he very solicitously sent to see if she needed help. It was through money from his own pocket that she kept alive. He used to say, however, that she actually saved him money: "I could never get any janitor to keep his eye on the building for the kind of hours she puts in."

And there was Tim, who probably wouldn't have been able to stay alive very long either, not for lack of food, but for want of what he called "a wee drop of the blessed stuff." Every Tuesday afternoon at four o'clock he very ceremoniously called at the side door of the episcopal residence, and was shown into the Bishop's private suite, where that kindly man was generally waiting for him. The Bishop would, with totally unnecessary caution, go over to each of the blinds and pull them down so that no one could see in, reach for the bottom lower left drawer of his desk, and extract a half-filled bottle of Old Smuggler. There would be the usual joke about Tim's having "an honest face" and so being permitted to hold the bottle, while the Bishop got the glasses. Then, with a few minutes of the most enjoyable conversation of the whole week, the Bishop would have a drink with Tim.

And there were others, too many to count, but people the Bishop called "the finest Catholics in the diocese."

One day in response to the young Chancellor's repeated pleas for a reform of the diocesan business policies, the Bishop granted him the authority to set up some badly needed administrative offices, to initiate sound legal procedures, and give the diocesan bookkeeping a good going over.

After this was successfully begun, the Chancellor turned his attention to a problem that had always irked him: the way Charity had been handled in the diocese.

To put it frankly, the old Bishop was everywhere known as a "soft touch." Any person in the diocese who needed financial aid (and some who didn't) could be fairly sure of getting it if only he had the courage to make the visit to the episcopal residence. And some of those who made the visit, the Chancellor knew too well, were not even from Gerasa. No wonder the diocese could never show a cash reserve.

It was in response to such unbusinesslike methods that the Chancellor set up the brand new diocesan Office of Organized Charities.

But, as he well knew, merely setting up the office did not put Charity on a businesslike basis; he had to get an administrator to fill it, a top-notch executive with experience in the field of such things as fund-raising and promotion.

Such executives, the Chancellor was fond of observing, did not grow on trees; you had to be willing to pay a very good salary to attract such talent. The only way Gerasa would ever attract such talent, he said, was to offer something in the vicinity of $30,000 a year, a bold step he was willing to take. "You want Charity," he would say, "you got to pay for it."

There were many takers for the $30,000. The chancery saw a parade of men, all looking like they knew just how Charity worked.

The practised eye of the Chancellor saw through many as unfit for the job of Christian Charity; as the days went by the list of names was sifted until only a few were left. One of these was a broker who said he was from Wall Street; the next was an advertising man and he said he was from Madison Avenue; the last one was the Devil, and he was from Hell, only he didn't say he was, of course. He said his name was O'Houlihan, and added (quite truthfully) that he had come up the hard way. He explained that he had been on the board of trustees of every major firm on both Madison Avenue and Wall Street, and had come to that point in life where he just thought he'd like to give a little of his experience to his Church.

Even the practised eye of the Chancellor was no match for this kind of approach, especially since Mr. O'Houlihan had all kinds of proof for anything he was asked about.

The thing that really clinched the deal was O'Houlihan's plan for Charity in Gerasa. Together the Chancellor and he spent many happy hours dreaming of the day when Charity would be put on a better business basis.

The first thing the new executive did was to hire an efficient office staff—some assistants, three fast-typing secretaries, and a receptionist, who couldn't type but who was beautiful. High class people, they received good salaries too, but O'Houlihan said that in time the system would be so efficient that the diocese would actually be making money.

The new office set up by O'Houlihan was a most modern one, with every time-saving device. The place was lined with electronic computers. First there was SAINTCAP (Standard Automatic Income Notator—Charitable Appeals Processor). Then there was BADRAP (Binary Automatic Digital Reevaluator and Aptitude Programmer). But the one O'Houlihan was most fond of was ELEEMOSYNVAC. This was an enormous machine that ran along the whole west wall of the building. The reason O'Houlihan liked it so much was that he himself, out of his vast experience in game theory, had evolved the machine for the splendid job of being charitable to people. "Science is coming to the aid of Charity," he said. "Machines like ELEEMOSYNVAC enable us to see into the mind and heart of man with such precision that for the first time in history everyone will be rendered exactly what he is due. We have," he added, "taken the guess-work out of Charity."

All available information was fed into the machines on everyone in the diocese who might possibly come to ask for assistance. The idea was that anyone requesting a hand-out was asked to give all the reasons why he should be helped rather than the next fellow; the material was submitted to the vast fund of information already stored in the machines, and then after a whirring of wheels and a flashing of lights, out popped a little card saying "Reject," or stating exactly the right amount of charity that ought to be dispensed.

It was a typical modern office in other ways, too. Everyone seemed to be handling a tremendous amount of official correspondence, and filling out forms. The receptionist at the desk in front of the door was one with much experience in handling people. She was extremely beautiful and sophisticated, a young thing who could always be relied upon to say the right things to the right people with exactly the right amount of warmth or chill. Some people said that she overdid it with the blood-red fingernail polish and the extra big earrings, for a Charity station, but then this is a matter of taste. What no one could deny was that she let only the right people in.

When the day came for the grand opening of the new Offices of Organized Charities, O'Houlihan had a big to-do about it, with members of both the religious and secular press attending. The old Bishop was there, very proud that so much was being done "for Christ's poor," as he said in a humble, moving little homily. After his talk, a previously selected poor person was brought up to ELEEMOSYNVAC, and the data on her situation fed into the machine. While the machine worked away at its multiplication and subtraction, the pretty receptionist took a huge scissors and cut a ribbon O'Houlihan had thoughtfully tied across the machine, to symbolize the beginning of Charity at Gerasa. The

ALL YE THAT THIRST
COME TO THE COMPUTER

photographers flashed their cameras again and again, and kept asking her to go through the operation one more time. And they started flashing again when the machine finally got ready to give its answer. After much interesting noise-making, the machine suddenly quieted, and out popped a little card, which even O'Houlihan was waiting to see. Only the old woman seemed unconcerned. It read simply, "Give the poor thing five hundred dollars." When this was read, a cheer went up from the multitude of notables present, and an insurance man burst into tears. Everyone was touched, and the papers all gave the event much coverage, most of them having a picture of the pretty receptionist and the ribbon, with the caption, "Charity starts off with a bang here."

The whole affair was very fine. The only thing that could be said against it was that it was the last time anyone was ever given any money by the diocesan Charities.

No one noticed it, of course, except O'Houlihan, and possibly the more alert members of the office staff, but the business of putting Charity on an independent basis in Gerasa seemed to consist mostly of saying no.

No matter what heart-rending data was poured into the ELEEMOSYNVAC machine, the little cards that popped out kept saying "Reject." Cases of motherless and fatherless broods of ten and twelve had no luck; a blind 80-year-old widow who was going to be thrown out of her house and who had cancer was given the same unqualified decision. Alcoholics, paraplegics, veterans wounded in their country's service, all got the same treatment, for the machine was nothing if not impartial, as O'Houlihan liked to say.

That is, everyone got the same treatment if they got past the receptionist. Most of them did not succeed in doing this. On the meeker applicants she simply used a certain frigid manner and a few high-sounding phrases, and this was enough to send them to the Salvation Army or Traveler's Aid. Those who had been poor a long time and who were made courageous by an empty stomach she immediately recognized, and started them on any of several buck-passing procedures invented by Mr. O'Houlihan in the inner office. These were usually of two types. In one, the person was bogged down filling out forms. If the person could not write, that automatically excluded him from any further assistance the diocesan office might give. If he did fill out all the forms, they turned out to be the wrong ones, or else they merely entitled him to a place "at the bottom of the list," a list which went for months without any change in positions. The hungry and poor generally could not stand much of this and did not come back.

Another procedure, to be used on the hale and fit, was to give them a form to take down to the "branch office." This was a five mile trudge, and when they got there they never had the right form—it was, in fact, nearly always a single letter or digit away from the magic one which would let loose the flow of plenty. The person always had to go back; and he had to keep on going back until he lost interest, or until he became so angry at the beautiful young receptionist that he had to be told by Mr. O'Houlihan to leave the premises with that sort of language and never come back again.

After a while the machine began to be very flippant about some of its replies. It also showed a definite tendency to use vulgar slang even when dealing with the most delicate family problems. Often the little card that popped out would bear no more of a message than something like "Drop dead" or "Get lost." On these occasions the staff member would say chidingly something to the effect that "you can't fool the machine, *it knows*." Then the pauper, or widow, or invalid who had the temerity to actually ask Organized Charities for help would be taken by the arm and led firmly out the door.

Mr. O'Houlihan was a great one for slogans and mottos, and so the office walls contained many quotations, including a number from Scripture. Some of the latter were remarkably free translations. For instance, "The poor you have always with you" was written as "The poor always keep hanging around." Some of the phrases really did not sound like Scripture at all, for example the one reading, "Be not too hasty to squander thy substance on the needy, lest he, turning upon thee, devour thee." Whenever O'Houlihan quoted this one he always mumbled that it was the Habacuc 5:18, knowing full well that as there is no fifth chapter to Habacuc, no one was ever likely to go home and prove him wrong. On the wall behind O'Houlihan's grinning face was his favorite quotation: "What the poor need more than bread or money / Is a thoughtful word both kind and funny."

So there was never any need to turn anyone away without some reference to the Bible telling them to accept their burden and not to envy those who have more than they do. Mr. O'Houlihan was a moving speaker when he got going on the subject of the futility of this world's possessions. If a man came in after his house burned down, O'Houlihan or one of his assistants would glance to the wall and rattle off something like "After crosses and losses men grow humbler and wiser.—Ben Franklin." Or if someone had made a costly financial blunder, putting him on the relief rolls, a staff member would conveniently read for him: "Failure to hit the bull's-eye is never the fault of the target; to improve your aim, improve yourself.—Arland Gilbert."

But it could never be said that a poor man stepped out of Organized Charities completely empty handed. Everyone, no matter who he was, had a great deal of difficulty leaving the office without having a loaf of bread pushed into his hands. O'Houlihan had a great supply of three-day-old bread stored away in the back rooms at all times, and the secretaries were instructed to make sure that no one left the office without having some of it forced upon him. Often in town you would come across a well-dressed but embarrassed businessman carrying a loaf of bread with the tell-tale proverbs all over it. ("Faith is like a wheelbarrow—you've got to put some push behind it to make it work."—Judson Kearns) And then you knew that he had just come from the chancery and hadn't been able to get to an ash can yet to dump it. Some of the more desperate people threw their bread right back at Mr. O'Houlihan, but they could never say it had not been offered.

After a while the city relief office started to complain to the Bishop of an influx of poor Catholics upon the rolls. The charts showed a sudden upsurge of cases right after Organized Charity had swung into action. The local Traveler's Aid station had to replenish its funds at an alarming rate; and the Salvation Army, after the biggest Christmas collection in its history, had to beat the drum again for more.

Even the mental hospital showed indications that something was drastically wrong with the public assistance program of Gerasa; people were being admitted at an incredible rate for insecurity and a feeling of not being wanted. At last the Mayor asked the Bishop to join him on a committee to find out what was causing a system to fall apart that had worked adequately for twenty-five years.

As soon as O'Houlihan heard of this he began a campaign saying that his budget was "unrealistic." "No comparable diocese in the land has the infinitesimal funds devoted to relief that Gerasa has," he said.

On radio and television he was granted time, to explain what he was trying to do for the city and why it could not possibly be done. "I need help, trained help," he said. "You just simply cannot expect *girls* to be able to come in and hold down desk jobs that really should be given to experienced public servants. Ever since the beginning, the diocesan program has been pock-marked by sham and hypocrisy. In addition, my hands are tied. If it weren't for the good Bishop, I swear I would have quit many times. And as for the rest, the diocese is beset by impossible petty rivalries and insubordination. I'll tell you what's wrong: I need money and I want it fast. The diocese has a half-million dollar investment up at Organized Charities, and I mean to protect it if it's the last thing I ever do in Gerasa!"

It was the last thing he ever did in Gerasa.

It took a long time, though, for the committee to get around to what it was talking about. For a long time it looked as if the committee never would. The Bishop and the Chancellor and the Mayor were all so anxious to help Charity along that it did not occur to them that anything deeply wrong existed.

But when the committee started hearing the testimony of witnesses, they became very alarmed. The Bishop was visibly moved when old Tim told of how the machine had refused to give him even so much as a dime for a cup of coffee, and had accused him of being an "old souse who wanted it for hooch."

Then some other witnesses told of the old lady dying of cancer, who was told by the machine to "drop dead" and then actually proceeded to do so.

Still other witnesses represented the broods of orphans refused assistance by the machine; and slowly the whole story of how the new office had failed to take care of Charity for Gerasa was told, from the mean receptionist at the door to the quotations of O'Houlihan on the walls.

But when O'Houlihan was brought before the committee he admitted that nothing was working right, and blamed it all on the machine. He said that after all, the machine wasn't infallible, and that it was not unusual for it to take a while getting started. The rest of the trouble he said was all traceable to the lack of sufficient funds.

It was while O'Houlihan was making his pitch for increased salaries that everything became clear all at once for the Bishop. He had long said that for some reason or other he felt compelled to hate this man, though he had never felt hatred for any other human being. All during O'Houlihan's long explanation of why no one could be given any help until January 1 of the succeeding year, a passage from Scripture kept occurring to the Bishop's mind over and over: "This kind is not driven out except by prayer and fasting."

As the meeting drew on toward the foregone conclusion of another salary increase for O'Houlihan and a renewed vote of confidence in his methods, asked for by the Chancellor, the time came for the signing of the contract. But under the pretext of bringing over the ink for the signing, the Bishop instead contrived to bring an old ink bottle that had holy water in it. With a silent promise to do later any prayer and fasting that might be necessary, and at the terrible risk of appearing ridiculous and childish in front of the Mayor and the important people of the diocese, the Bishop rather playfully dipped his finger in the bottle and flicked some holy water in O'Houlihan's face.

There was a blinding flash and a tremendous roar, and to this day no two people agree on what happened. But when it was over, there was no Charity Executive; no one knew where he had gone. The only damage from the explosion was that the magnificent stained glass window of St. Michael which dominated the conference room was blown outwards as if by some heavy projectile leaving the building. "His parting shot," the old Bishop used to say laughingly ever after.

the case of the surprised psychoanalyst

Now it happened at this time that there was a famous psychoanalyst who was among the number of men in that profession who do not believe in God. Whenever his patients mentioned the name of God, the psychoanalyst would say, "There is no God; God is a myth."

As he did not believe in God, it is not surprising that the psychiatrist did not believe in the Devil, either. He said, "There is no Devil; the Devil is a myth."

One day, not long after the adventures just narrated, the Devil decided to pay a visit to the psychoanalyst. He knew that he could not hope for much from human learning that would be applicable to his own case; however, he had heard of the wonders of psychoanalysis, and being interested in keeping up with things, wanted to see how it worked. And in spite of his better judgment, he held a lingering hope that something might after all come of it. Who knows, thought the Devil, the doctor might be able to release some of my inner tensions, and resolve some of my many conflicts. Or he might even be able to clear up this burning sensation I am plagued with.

When the Devil came for his appointment, the psychoanalyst asked him, "Who are you?"

"I am the Devil," the Devil replied.

"You are not the Devil," the analyst said at once, "you only think you are. People are coming into this office all the time and telling me strange things like that. Some of them think they are God, and others think they are Napoleon. Now you probably think that you are the first one ever to think he was the Devil. But you're not—three of my patients in the past had the idea long before you.

"However," he continued, "if you will cooperate with me, I am sure I can turn you once again into a healthy citizen, eager to take your place in society."

The Devil became very upset at being told that he was not the Devil. And he was further irritated by the talk about being an eager citizen. But it appeared that if he was going to be permitted to pour out his troubles, he would have to go along with the doctor a bit. He insisted once more that he *was* the Devil, but after that he let the subject drop.

Or he tried to. It kept cropping up, though, in everything they talked about. Every time the analyst asked him to recall things from his past, the events were all mixed up with what the doctor kept calling "myths," and on top of that, most of them happened so many millions of years ago that the analyst felt he was being made a fool of.

"Myths!" he cried, "nothing but myths. All I ask is that you recall your childhood, you don't have to give me a history of the universe."

By this time both doctor and patient were becoming more and more irritated with one another. Finally the

Devil mentioned something about his adventures in the Garden of Eden, and the analyst lost his professional manner completely. "Go ahead, gibber away," he said, throwing down his pencil. "But there's no reason why I should knock myself out trying to take this stuff down."

The Devil kept talking. He spoke of his first million years. Then he went on to his second million. He was about to go on to the third, when something in his account caught the attention of the exhausted analyst. "Wait a minute," said the analyst, "who's this 'he' you keep mentioning?" It was plain that the Doctor thought himself on the trail of an Oedipus Complex, or at least, a sibling rivalry.

"God," said the Devil.

"Aha," replied the analyst, feeling that he had discovered something at last, "you are a religionist. It is the God concept that is at the bottom of all your troubles." With this new evidence, the doctor settled himself down to give the patient some insight into the case. "Allow me to explain religion away for you."

"Religion," he continued, in familiar territory, "is akin to an obsessional neurosis of children. It is a collective neurosis. The God concept, the illusion of a fatherly God, is a failure to face reality. When you were a child (at this Lucifer's face took on a puzzled look) you were confronted with dangerous, uncontrollable and ununderstandable forces both within and outside yourself. (At this the confusion grew even more apparent on the Devil's face.) Nevertheless, you felt yourself protected by a father you thought to be of superior wisdom and strength. (Here it was plain that the Devil was no longer mentally with the doctor; he was in fact trying to recall what he knew of the various symptoms of mental illness, to see if he could figure out where he fitted in.) As you grew up and became a man, you were once again faced with fearful forces; but you do not want to face them alone. You regress, you bring back your father in the image of an all-powerful God. What do you think of that?"

After this little declamation the analyst naturally wanted to hear his patient's reaction. The doctor was at last hopeful that they were making progress. He sat up, waiting to hear what the patient would say.

"Tell me about Paranoia," the Devil said. "Sometimes I think I manifest some of the symptoms."

This remark showed such a total lack of appreciation of all that the analyst had been trying to say that he wondered for a moment why he had ever become a doctor. His Super Ego triumphed, however, and soon he was hard at work again, trying to figure out something that would rescue the patient from his delusions.

The analyst was at a considerable loss as to what to do. Talking was obviously of no use; but that gave the doctor another idea: maybe the patient would like to act out his problems.

"How about having a Psycho-drama?" he asked. "You figure out a little play, you see, and take one part in it. By observing how you react, we will learn a valuable lesson on how your mind works."

The Devil was delighted; he said something about liking very much the school of Elia Kazan, and then he was ready to go.

The Devil put on quite a show. Instead of a simple little Psycho-drama, it was a magnificent production, all full of quotations from *Paradise Lost,* from Dante, and

from Goethe's *Faust.* As the analyst sat there behind his desk, he was quite carried away, for the acting of the Devil was so deeply moving that it seemed almost as if the house lights had dimmed and the curtain gone up on a full cast with chorus and orchestra.

The story the Devil chose was the age-old tragedy of Unbending Pride. The analyst was on the edge of his chair as he heard the way his patient screamed defiance at the heavens, while the very room shook to the battle between the Sons of Darkness and the Sons of Light. Several times as the battle turned, the analyst found himself jumping and yelling, shouting at the top of his voice for the patient's hard-pressed army, screaming that they must fight back, and that they must not fall into the abyss. And during the long deep fall into the black eternal night, the doctor had the feeling that he was there physically, that he was falling too, and as he fell he learned the meaning of eternity the way his patient knew it. And he thought he caught some of the deeper meaning of other words, such as frustration and rejection—and hate, too. Through the whole play there ran a constant theme of hate.

But the play had no end; it just petered out, and there were the two of them, doctor and patient, sitting looking at one another. For a while the doctor was almost overcome with sympathy for the patient, now that he knew the terrible burden he bore. The patient's tale of woe and misery was almost enough to make a man believe in Hell.

For a while they just sat, wondering where to go from there. Then the analyst decided that the time had come to be positive. "You know the purpose of all this, don't you? The purpose of psychoanalytic treatment is to restore or give to the patient the capacity to love."

The mention of the word *love* had a strong effect on Lucifer. All that had gone before had shown him that whatever analysis could do for humans, it was not for him. Indeed the hopelessness of his case had just been borne in upon him with great clarity, as he was acting out the psycho-drama. Then the doctor had begun his foolish prattle about love, that the purpose of everything was to give the devil the capacity to love. All at once the Devil was taken hold of by an overpowering hatred of the little analyst and all his talk.

At this point the doctor, most surprisingly, began to experience delusions. First he had the utterly inexplicable sensation that his patient's head was growing larger. The doctor screamed and held his hands over his eyes, but when he looked through the cracks in his fingers he could see that the delusion was still there, growing larger even, and more pronounced than ever. The head was enormous now, and it was plainly the head of a giant lizard. Really it was the jaws that made the head so large, great mandibles just like those of a Tyrannosaurus Rex, the gigantic Thunder Lizard of the past, and they had rows of white teeth disappearing between folds of flesh.

Suddenly, as the analyst was looking up unbelievingly at the head of the delusion, now well on its way toward the ceiling and knocking the chandelier around every time it moved, he was surprised by a little swishing sound by his chair. (The delusion is affecting my hearing as well as my sight, he noted carefully.) He turned, and saw it was the Delusion's tail, nervously groping around the room, flitting back and forth, as if it were looking for something.

All this time the doctor had the impression that the evil little eyes of the Delusion never stopped staring at him, looking down at him as though he were nothing more than a morsel to eat, saliva dripping down onto its great scaley chest. To escape the swishing tail of the Delusion the analyst jumped up onto the desk, realizing that if anyone saw him he would certainly appear ridiculous acting this way in front of a patient. But he did so anyway, as it was plain that the tail was beginning to look for him now, and was even feeling its way around the chair he had just left.

All this time the Delusion had kept rather quiet; but it was not a peaceful quiet—it was the hostile silence of a cold-blooded animal surveying the landscape. The doctor would have kept talking if he could, to keep in spite of everything the right physician-patient relationship so essential to therapy, but really since the Delusion had set in it had been very difficult to think of anything to say.

"I'm certainly glad that the Devil is only a myth," said the analyst to himself, breathing heavily, for he could see that the thing was coiling up a bit as if to spring. "Otherwise, I certainly would be in a terrible position."

Then, however, after the Delusion had apparently reached its full growth, and occupied three-fourths of the room, it roared.

It was truly a tremendous roar, just like those of the jungle beasts you hear at the zoo, when they roar so powerfully and low that you wonder how their chests and lungs can stand it, the kind of roar that makes you start wondering if the bars are really strong enough to hold all that fury inside the cages. When the psychoanalyst heard this mighty sound his manner changed, and he said to himself, "I have never heard a patient roar like this before. This is no ordinary patient."

Alas, however, that was as close to a diagnosis as the poor man could come, for in the very next instant the Devil leaped upon him and destroyed him utterly, so that there was absolutely nothing left of him, not even his cufflinks.

His treatment thus concluded, the Devil gave up all hope of therapy and left the Doctor's office. Then he walked abroad once more as a raging lion, and roamed through the world, seeking the ruin of souls.

babel

Now in those days the people of the little midwestern town of Babel said to themselves, "Let us build ourselves a school system, so great that it will make Babel famous, so that the fame thereof will spread throughout the land."

They decided to start with a High School, and began to plan how it was going to be built, down to the last detail. But for a while it looked as though everything would be wrecked right away, because the Negroes started lobbying for a non-segregated school. This threat was however successfully handled when the white people gave in, although most of them didn't want to, but knew they had to, or else go without the school. (Since there weren't very many Negroes in Babel anyway, it really didn't make much difference to them.)

So the segregation problem looked just about solved in Babel when a man by the name of Jasper came into town, carrying a kind of carpet bag with him. He said that something was taking place in Babel that was an evil thing. He said that the mixing of races was an abomination before the Lord, and that its stench reached to high heaven.

Mr. Jasper was a kind of preacher-prophet, but in addition to this, he turned out to be something of an anthropologist, too, and called himself *Doctor* Jasper. He had charts and things in his carpet bag, and in no time at all had set up study clubs and adult education courses, and he went around the streets in a loud-speaker truck preaching his doctrines to anyone who would listen.

There were a lot of people who listened. With these he formed White Citizens Clubs to study the problem, and to look at his charts.

They were most unusual charts. The biology teacher from the university said that they were unlike any she'd ever seen in a classroom. All the other ones on the human race, she said, traced Man back to a common ancestor. It didn't flatter Man very much, but it did make everybody brothers.

But Dr. Jasper was a devilish clever fellow, and knew a lot more than any old school teacher did. He had a chart for everything, and on his charts, Man was definitely not of one race. Some men descended from one prehistoric animal, while others descended from others. The White Race, for instance, was pictured going back through a long series of cave-men, until it connected up with a tribe of very intelligent looking African monkeys. At first this seemed annoying to some White folks, until they saw what the other races were traced back to. Then they were happy, because at least there were no snakes and lizards in their ancestry.

The charts and things did not take long to cause excitement. In a short time, the few Negroes in Babel were run out of town, and work was begun on the High School—which was to be a completely segregated one now.

But Dr. Jasper didn't leave town. He stayed on with his work, "educating the people of Babel."

He said the Negroes weren't the only ones. He said that actually it was only a popular misconception that the Negroes were the only inferior race. In reality, the White Race itself was only a name given to a lot of people who *looked* alike, and this covered up all sorts of things.

One day he startled a mass-meeting in the Armory by screaming at them, "There is only one thing that is worse than being black. And that one thing is *being too white!* It's worse than not being white at all!"

Then he showed them how a "different breed" had penetrated their ranks, a breed that did not belong—odd people, people who were whiter than a person should be. They were sallow, sickly looking creatures who had *passed* as normal white people for so long that everyone had grown calloused to their evil, scheming ways. Then he jumped over the footlights down into the audience, pointing out exactly who the pale people were.

"Most of us," he said, after he had singled out these unfortunate individuals, "have had the good fortune to have been born of a normal ruddy complexion. (His voice was choked with emotion as he said this, and very humble.) Let those of us who have been so gifted with normal red blood be grateful; let us act the part; let us not defile our lives by any contact with the sub-normal, with the sickly pale; let us cast them out from us, no matter who they may be. And let us be swift about it, for in a matter such as this, quickness is the only true mercy."

As he talked, there was a great deal of nervous shifting around in the audience. People began craning their necks to see how many pallid persons there were near them. Others, obviously pale to begin with, got even paler as the proceedings continued, as Dr. Jasper went on about the terrible crime rate of the pale folk. He said that statistics for the last two decades showed that more than 85% of all crimes occurring in the U.S. were committed by the pale-complexioned, a sin-prone race if there ever was one. Another table he referred to showed conclusively that the too-white were the most unlikely to own their own homes, were deepest in debt, had most broken marriages, filled most of the insane asylums, and were confirmed slum-dwellers.

As the crowd left the Armory after the meeting, they unconsciously began to separate into groups: some were the people who were all rosy-cheeked, and others were the predominant shades who were noticeably on the lighter side. It was in these groups that the first organization along the new color lines made itself felt. Dr. Jasper, talking with the more upset among the ruddy-complexioned, said he would be glad to lead them in their fight to keep the race clean. But the too-white people weren't wasting any time, either. If anything, they were better organized faster, for they had the sense of urgency that the state of siege brings on.

From the beginning, they adopted the policy that it was they who were right and the other fellows wrong. They refused to put up with the names that Jasper tried to hang on them when he called them pallid and bloodless, and instead called themselves the Pure Whites. There could be no doubt, they said, that if anyone represented the true human race it was the White Man, and of the White Man, who could be the best element except the whitest of all, namely themselves?

They caused a lot of trouble. There weren't quite

so many of them around as there were of the others, and so they had a tendency to gang together and be troublesome. They even started moving into neighborhoods together, sending real estate values plunging. A lot of normal people lost money in these affairs, and real fear and hatred sprang up over it.

Normal people were afraid to go near the ghettos the Pale People formed. If a normal person was found in that territory after dark, he was taking his life into his own hands, people used to say.

Delinquency went up. Gang wars now occurred regularly, along the new racial lines.

Even seating in street cars and busses became a problem. No one wanted to sit next to a pallid person, and so certain sections of each vehicle were designated "For Pure Whites Only." But that didn't work, and so they ended up by dividing the whole transportation system. It was very aggravating for a normal person to wait fifteen minutes for a bus, only to have the bus turn out to be one that was marked for the sub-normal. But that was how Dr. Jasper said it had to be, and he was running things in Babel.

By the use of such stringent methods, however, the pale people were pretty well fenced off from the rest of the population after a while, and practically put on reservations, and it looked as though Babel was at last headed for some well-needed peace.

But there was, surprisingly, no peace. Among the ones who were left, it wasn't enough just to know you were "allright" and belonged truly to the human race. Everyone's conscience had now been aroused, and everyone wanted to know more about where he stood. Study groups became popular, with Dr. Jasper in great demand. In all his talks, Dr. Jasper insisted that the totals weren't all in yet, and that a final reckoning still had to be made as to the essential definitions of terms such as "race," "color," "human," and so forth. There were indications, he said, that the final results might surprise everybody.

And so gradually people of a similar hue and blend naturally stuck together more and more, and studied anthropology very hard under the Doctor's guidance, each group hoping desperately that the final decision would show that *they* were the realest of the real.

But the more the question was studied, the more it became a matter of pigment. And this manifested itself in other ways, too, in the color of a person's eyes, or hair. As soon as this became known, a few irresponsible red-heads somehow picked up the notion that it was all a plot against them, to keep them out of things. Tempers flared and fists flew, and pretty soon the red-heads got up in a huff and formed their own organization. They said that they could draw charts as well as anybody else, and on their charts, needless to say, the red-heads were in a very good position; they had all the best ancestors, with a line of magnificently red-haired cavemen joining a line of very intelligent looking red-headed gorillas, back around 1 million B.C. They also claimed that Julius Caesar was a red-head.

Another group that didn't get along very well with Dr. Jasper was the darkly tanned crowd. Now everybody knows that there is no one on this earth who is more apt to be proud and conceited and generally insufferable than the person who spends all his energies trying to get a good sun tan. And if there is one thing the professional sun bather despises it is to have someone ignore the rich tone of his skin. When Dr. Jasper did not come out early for the well tanned, and say that they should inherit the earth, he immediately lost them, and they went off to form their own race. They had spent their whole lives turning to a rich golden brown, they said, and if anyone was now going to even hint that they would have been better off to remain the way they were it was just too much to take, for you might as well tell them they had wasted their whole lives.

But Dr. Jasper didn't worry about the splinter groups. He was busy in his laboratory, tracking down the last identifying characteristics that would determine who was normal and who was not. At last he announced that his unprecedented labors had been "crowned with success." A mass meeting was called to hear the results and the nature of his discovery.

When the huge throng had gathered in the Armory, and around it, for it overflowed into the streets, everyone quieted to hear the all-important information.

"It is now clear," Dr. Jasper announced, in a slow, solemn and stately manner, "beyond a shadow of a doubt, and proved by clinical research, that the human race is divided according to . . . (here he paused to find the place in his notes; after he did this he picked up the glass of water on the speaker's stand and sipped it thoughtfully; he looked as though he would have gone on just standing there, but the angry tumult that arose from the many thousands waiting for an answer to all their doubts forced him to continue) . . . is divided, I say, not as it were, vertically, according to pigmentation merely, but horizontally, as it were, by facial characteristics."

The crowd went mad at this. What it came down to was that it all had to do with things like noses and ears, and not just color. People with big noses belonged to one racial type, while those with big ears belonged to another, as also did those with ears and noses that were not big enough. Only those with *normal* sized ears and noses, Dr. Jasper said, could be classified as fully human.

This announcement, as might be expected, caused no little regrouping in the hall. People could be seen standing with dazed expressions on their faces, feeling their noses and ears and measuring them with their fingers. All of a sudden the size of one's nose or ears became of capital importance, and no longer anything to joke about.

After the meeting, naturally many people rushed up to ask Dr. Jasper if their ears were too big or too small, or if their noses were too prominent or not noticeable enough to "belong." And it was a funny thing with Dr. Jasper: when he was talking to someone who had big ears, it somehow seemed as though his own ears grew and grew until they were flapping there in the wind and he looked like the leader of all the big-eared people on earth. But if he was talking to someone who had a very big nose, why then the Doctor's nose would accommodate, and would stretch a little with every word he spoke, until it was very long, the longest nose you ever did see. The result was that everyone went home happy, feeling that he was on the winning side, and that whatever happened, he would be all right, for his nose and his ears were just about the same size as Dr. Jasper's.

But when they got home, of course, they met people

who claimed the very same thing for their side of the question, and who had to be set right. And so it was that house was set against house, and husbands against wives, and parents against children, for it is no surprising thing that each member of a family does not have exactly the same style ears and nose that the others have.

And so all kinds of new groups sprang up; every conceivable type of face and build was represented, and each group was sure that Dr. Jasper was their leader and the finest example of their type.

Where all this became most evident was in the affair over the status of the new High School. With all the new races running around in Babel, it was easy to see that it was going to be no simple job naming who could use the school and who couldn't. Of course only the Normal People would be allowed to send their children to it, but since everyone thought he was normal, there were going to be an awful lot of disappointed parents around when school opened.

Dr. Jasper declared privately to each group that a drive would have to be staged, a campaign to save the school for the Normal People. He confidentially told each group that he of course was on their side, but that he needed their help to save the school for them, and that they would have to run a really strong propaganda drive to be successful.

By this time the Legion Brothers had found their way to Babel, and they came into the city by train, bus and airplane. They were everywhere, only of course you had to know what to look for to recognize them—they were well hidden under the most elaborate disguises. Soon each one was leading a different group, and it was plain that they were having a fine time and were happy to be out of Hell. And after they arrived, it was no time at all before things really began to get exciting.

At once everybody was taken up with the propaganda drive. Everywhere you went, people were painting signs, or fixing up public address systems, or practicing speeches.

You had to rely on rumors and hearsay as to which way things were going. One day you'd hear that they were going to run the people with green eyes out of town; but then you'd see a green-eyed person walking around in broad daylight, and he'd laugh, and say, no, it was the brown-eyed finally got it, the way he'd heard. The radio was useless for this kind of information, as it changed hands so often. There was all kinds of dashing around, with handbills being stuck under doors, speakers standing on soap-boxes, and people making uniforms that they would wear to identify themselves for their own group.

Reporters came to Babel from all parts of the country. Mobile television units were constantly interviewing citizens of Babel, giving the nation at large some idea of the tense and excited atmosphere of the city on the eve of its High School fight. The town square took on a festive appearance (which was certainly misleading for no one was in a mood to celebrate anything) with various slogans strung around lamp posts and arching across the streets near the square. One would read "Save our school for the Thin People," while the next would say "The Skinny People must go!"

One attractive young blond was carrying a sign that said, "For the Blond-headed Atheists!"—and when

DO YOU WANT YOUR SISTER TO MARRY A BLOND ??
WIPE OUT THE YOUNG
ONLY WE ARE WORTHY

questioned by newsmen she said yes, she was an atheist in addition to being blond. But there didn't seem to be any other blond-headed atheists around. Judging by the signs, there were short atheists and tall ones, thin ones and fat, but they were each carrying their own banners, and pushing their own causes, and they didn't get along at all.

One man had a huge placard he was waving for the television cameras that read "Down With Everybody But the Near-sighted Free-Thinkers!" Doubtless he himself was a Freethinker, for it was quite obvious that he was near-sighted.

Quite a fight developed in one of the alleys near the square. A large group of Blue-eyed partisans were marching triumphantly through the alley when a very determined batch of people having steel-gray eyes entered it from the opposite direction. After the fight was over there were enough black eyes to form an entirely new group, if anyone had wanted.

Then at last the day came that Dr. Jasper had set for the decision about the school. A huge throng formed in the square with Dr. Jasper in the center of it, speaking through a microphone. He said a few words against "mongrelization of the races," just to get everybody tuned up and into the feel of things, and then shouted directions for the march to the High School, to decide once and for all "who gets it."

The mob moved out toward the school, led by Dr. Jasper, and of course the Legion Brothers, too, who kept shouting encouragement to all sides. Then the crowd became so unruly that even Dr. Jasper was lost sight of, and everybody rushed toward the building.

But someone had got up early that day and had

beaten everybody else to it: it was a little man with a gasoline can, and he was standing in the school yard admiring his handiwork when the rest of them got there. There really was no High School left, properly speaking, by this time—just the flames shooting high into heaven, and the little man standing there, saying over and over, to nobody in particular, "If the people who have freckles don't get it, *nobody* does." You could see his own freckles quite clearly reflected in the fierce light of the blaze.

Babel is gone now, and you hardly ever hear mention of it any more. Oh, from time to time a humorist will bring it into one of his jokes, because even the name of the place is sure to get a laugh; but for the most part, these are only the very poor comedians.

the contact man

Along about this time there chanced to fall into the Devil's hands a copy of a small, uplifting magazine called "Happy Days." Although the magazine at first glance appeared to be a religious one, it was not, really.

Perhaps the best way to describe it is to say that it was "wholesome." It stood for all sorts of wholesome things: it was strongly in favor of good health; even more strongly it was for cheerfulness, and it had its own brand of self-help psychology by which readers were to pull themselves up out of every emotional valley, no matter how deep. The magazine was also in favor of Heaven—almost solely, however, in its capacity to make the flowers bloom.

To buttress these things the magazine had a formidable supply of pleasant poems, and another supply, almost as formidable, of pleasant jokes. The jokes were not funny, they were pleasant. For illustration, it depended rather heavily on paintings of houses by the side of the road, with plenty of hollyhocks. Sometimes there were trellises of roses, but the artists soon got back to their hollyhocks. And by actual count, no less than 34% of the articles in the magazine were about Thomas A. Edison—usually in his youth, overcoming an obstacle by the use of plain old common sense. In fact, there was hardly anything the magazine was more strongly in favor of than good old common sense.

However, at the time when it came to the Devil's attention, the magazine was really not doing too well. The circulation was slipping, and even the very active imagination of its promotion department could not sustain it. The copy writers worked their brains overtime to think up catchy expressions such as "*Happy Days* is here again!" or "*Happy Days* is just around the corner!" But in a world full of Cold War, rising prices and hidden taxes, subscribers were turning into a cynical bunch who knew of better things to do with their money.

One day those in charge of the magazine had a meeting and said, "Our cheerful magazine is slipping. If we lose any more subscribers *Happy Days* is done for. Let us therefore bring in an expert who will tell us how to run a magazine. He will make the magazine slick and readable, and the circulation will rise."

So the cheerful magazine hired an expert. He was an expert, everyone said, but no one knew at what. He spoke of "angles" and "schmaltz," of "dumbing it down," and of "sharpening it up." But most of all he spoke of contacts.

He said that what he really was was a contact man, first, last, and always. He said you couldn't run a magazine these days unless you had contacts, and knew the right people.

He knew all the right people, he said, and was going to fix it so that the editors would all know the right people, too. "You can't run a magazine from the Corn Belt," he would say, "but if you're going to try, you need plenty of contacts back in New York."

The Contact Man was only rarely at the magazine;

he was always out making contacts. This required an enormous salary, because he was so good at it. But he said that simply by sealing envelopes differently in the mailing rooms the little magazine would save enough on glue alone to pay his salary. (However his expense account was something else again; it would have taken an awful lot of glue to pay for that.)

Whenever the Contact Man would drop in at the editorial offices, everything would stop, and everybody would listen to what he had to say about what was going on in the wonderful world of publishing. Life on these occasions for the editors developed into one long conversation that drifted out of the Contact Man's office into the other rooms, and back again; and even when the Contact Man wasn't there the editors were continually talking about who was going to pull something big in the business. Often the Contact Man would take the editor or one of the others with him to New York, to make the contacts which were going to do the little magazine a world of good.

However, in spite of all this, the little magazine kept slipping. The editors were kept extremely busy renewing the contacts that their man had begun, and sometimes there really wasn't anyone home to do any work. As this kept on, and none of the contacts seemed to be helping the little magazine as much as they were expected to, the editors finally had to tell the Contact Man that he would have to do something soon, or *Happy Days* would be gone forever.

He had expected for a long time that things would come to this, and so he had saved up his best contact for last. It was a contact he didn't let everybody in on, he said, but since the editors were extra-special friends of his, he was going to make this contact for them.

The contact he referred to was an individual who took special interest in down-and-out magazines; he did it as a challenge, because he was so good at it. Everyone called him The Master, because he was such a master craftsman, and because he had such unbelievable command over circulation tricks. The Master drove a hard bargain, the Contact Man said, and it was almost like selling your soul to do business with him, but that was the price you had to pay to get the best. "One thing," he advised them, "be sure to go along with whatever The Master suggests. He doesn't like to do business with people who hem and haw. The Master will want a free hand; if there is anything that gets him upset it's for someone to ask for his help, and then go making conditions. In fact, it would be well not to say much of anything at all; you people aren't in any condition to go telling him how you want things run."

The Master turned out to be much easier to deal with than they expected, from the talk of the Contact Man. The first thing he did was to guarantee them in writing an annual increase of 200,000 for the first three years, and he also stated that if they did not make a 10% annual profit they could call off the whole deal. In return for this, he demanded that production of the magazine be moved to his own superbly equipped plant in New York, leaving only advertising, circulation fulfillment, and letters from readers back at the offices in the Corn Belt. After 6 years, the editors could have their magazine back, if they wanted it.

The editors were extremely proud to have pulled off such a deal. At last, they felt, the Contact Man had put them on to something good. As for himself, the

HAPPY DAYS

Contact Man seemed to sense that his job had been done when he put them in contact with The Master; with The Master working for them, they didn't need any other help, and so he discreetly withdrew, to make new contacts elsewhere, and to tell other editors of the wonderful things that happen in the world of publishing.

The first word the editors had of the success of the new *Happy Days* magazine was from a review of it in a trade publication. The commentator, who was quite well respected, said,

> We think the new *Happy Days* is a tremendous contribution to contemporary journalism. Although just a trifle too clever (diabolically clever, one might say) in spots, everything about this first issue indicates that it is being done by real pros. We really relish the Satanic glee with which it goes about poking fun at some of our most stuffy institutions, which have hitherto been foolishly regarded as above criticism. It refuses to accept anything as sacred, and insists on demolishing the shibboleths of modern day society.
>
> Although the name *Happy Days* has been retained, the title has taken on a new, sophisticated, somewhat facetious quality—this magazine is not for children anymore. Judging from the risqué tone that runs right through it, *Happy Days* certainly should no longer have any circulation problems. We congratulate the editors on the way they have caught up with the times. Who says you can't run a magazine from the Corn Belt?

With such a review, the interest of the editors was naturally greatly aroused, and some of them felt rather concerned with some of the statements. They anxiously waited for a look at the first issue.

In the meantime, however, they were kept busy answering letters from readers, which had increased enormously. Of course, in any change of this sort, editors expect "crank" letters and cancellations, and this case was no exception.

Meanwhile, back at The Master's headquarters, the Legion Brothers were happily putting out their first magazine. Each one had something to add, but of course, as usual, the most brilliant idea was one of Lucifer's: "One of the things that absolutely must go into it," he said, "is one of those advice columns. I've always felt that I could do a better job than Ann Landers anyway." And while he was busy thinking up advice for his column, the others worked at their specialties, too. The Legion Brother in charge of articles scheduled some very provocative ones; indeed they became more and more provocative with each issue. *Happy Days* became a wild storm center of dispute and discussion. No opinion, no matter how unusual or shocking, was too bold for the new magazine. Frequently the Post Office would refuse to handle an issue because of the nature of one or more of the articles, but this did not seem to hurt circulation any; the next issue that made the mails would have double the readership. But if the articles were frank, it would be best not even to go into the new photography and the new art work provided by the Legion Brothers in charge of those things. And the fiction—well, the fiction was perhaps worst of all. But so it seemed with every other aspect of the new *Happy Days*. Each Legion Brother was so good at his specialty that it was hard to say which one was responsible for the most breathless advance.

It was a strange thing, however, that everybody else saw the new magazine before the editors did, back in the Corn Belt. Of course, living out there away from where everything was going on, it was to be expected that there would be a time lag. But week after week went by, and everybody else in the country seemed to be acquainted with the new *Happy Days* but them; there they sat, disconsolate, the only editors in the country who did not know what their own magazine looked like.

They dispatched a sharp note to The Master telling him that they did not like being left out of things, but got no reply. Indeed, the only way they were able to keep in contact at all with what was happening to their magazine was through the letters from readers, but this was very unsatisfactory, as there was so much variance in opinion, and half the time the editors didn't know what the readers were talking about anyway.

At first, the mail was split, half in favor of the new magazine, and half opposed. Many of the old timers who had been taking *Happy Days* since the Great Blizzard of '88 cancelled their subscription. They wanted to know what had become of the old *Happy Days*; they said that down through the years it had lifted them out of countless blue spells, but now it seemed to be bent on causing even more trouble than there already was in the world. After the old timers had all cancelled out, the mail for a long time was nothing but praise. Even though the editors didn't have much to do with it any more, they could not help but feel proud the way everybody praised *Happy Days*—even other editors, really good ones, said that they were certainly doing a good job. They gave advice now freely to other publications, advising them with a new-found confidence on all the intricacies of promotion and envelope-sealing. They told of how important contacts were, and said to other editors that any time a contact was needed, just to let them know, for they had a great deal of influence in some surprising places.

Then suddenly there was a noticeable change in the mail. Slowly the complaints increased, and began to exceed the praises. And when there *was* praise now, it always seemed to come from unwanted sources. All the letters written on stationery and neatly done contained criticism; all the letters with scurrilous language and illegible writing were full of praise.

When this was first noticed, the editors became very much concerned, more so than at any time previous. They consumed aspirin and drank coffee, in between urgent messages to New York. Then after a while some of them switched from coffee to something stronger. The mail kept coming in though, until the favorable letters amounted usually only to an obscene word or two, and the critical ones came from every corner of the country—from statesmen, bishops, teachers, and finally, from the Post Office. This last letter said that as the character of *Happy Days* placed it outside of those categories which the department was permitted to carry by law, no more copies would be handled unless evidence was given of a changed policy.

At this, the editors finally swung into action. They decided to go to New York and confront The Master. That is, those who were in shape to go; three of them had become alcoholics from drinking between telegrams; several of the others had ulcers from worry; and a few more had come down with psychoses because of their repeated attempts to visualize the absent magazine—they went around the office staring at a spot directly in front of them, saying "I see it, I see it! Our cheerful publication is back, *Happy Days* is here again!"

That brought the number down to three, and they took off for New York.

As soon as the three surviving editors reached New York, you can be sure that they hurried to the address of The Master. They had some difficulty finding it, for they were looking for a large building, perhaps a whole skyscraper devoted to just one company; but when they found it, it was a surprisingly small and even dingy establishment. A sign in gaudy gold lettering read "Legion Bros. Publishers." And in smaller letters, "Represented Throughout the World."

Inside, the appearances were even less prepossessing. The whole place had about it the atmosphere of an Armenian rug merchant's, and as the editors came in, although they could not see anybody they had the impression that they were being scrutinized by several pairs of eyes from between the rugs. This as a matter of fact turned out to be pretty much the case, and as soon as the pairs of eyes saw who the visitors were, the individuals who owned them came out from behind the rugs and were recognized as the Legion Brothers themselves. They were a bit embarrassed, and apologized, and said "It doesn't pay to be careless in this line. What can we do for you?"

The editor-in-chief was so confused by this time that he almost forgot to be angry; but then he very determinedly began to tell the Legion Brothers that he wanted to see his magazine, and he wanted to know what was coming off. But while he was talking, The Master himself hurried into the room and scooped up a bunch of curtains, which had been used as office partitions (that was what the editors had mistaken for rugs). He was in a tremendous hurry, hardly even noticing the editors, and it became obvious at this point that the Legion Brothers had been interrupted in the midst of moving day. "This is something we learned from the Gypsies," The Master said when he finally noticed the guests. "With curtains you can be gone in half an hour." And he continued rapidly taking down curtains and laying them over his arm while he was talking.

The editor started in again to say that he wanted to know what was happening, and would like to see some copies of his magazine. But by this time all the Legion Brothers were taking down curtains too; "He wants to see his magazine," said one Legion Brother to another as they both were taking down a huge purple curtain; "Show the man his magazine," said the other, between folds. And then both disappeared under the curtain as they carried it into the back room.

"What has become of my magazine?" pleaded the editor in an agonized voice when The Master came back for another load of drapes, "What have you done with it?" The Master, his lips clamped together on safety pins, and his arms filled with drapes, tried as best he could to tell him, by shaking and nodding his head vigorously. But soon he was gone, too, with the others, into the back room. The editor followed them in, for it was plain that they were making off with his magazine right under his nose. But when he got there a most horrifying spectacle greeted him, for the Legion

Brothers were opening a trap door in the floor, and as they opened it blinding rays of light shot out from it and played back and forth on the ceiling. "Do you want to come with us?" said one of the Legion Brothers, laughing. "Come on along–*Happy Days* is going underground and we could use an old experienced hand." Then they started climbing down into the heat and glare.

The horrified editor shrank back, terrified of the sulphurous boilings and the flames that shot up from the opening. And then he did a very extraordinary thing, but it must be remembered that he really was not himself, and had been under a severe strain for many months. He saw the trap-door start to close on his poor little magazine, and at the last moment, to the great consternation of the other two editors, he flung himself into the pit.

Shocked as they were, the other two editors decided against following him. But going back to the Corn Belt didn't sound like much of an idea either, so they just stayed in New York. Though a poor place to visit, they observed, it was a fine place to live.

the good old days

One day the Devil got himself a gold-headed cane and a banker's suit, and a black Cadillac and a chauffeur, and drove up to the Conservative Athletes Association. He did not have any trouble getting in, because of the gold-headed cane and the Cadillac, even though he did not look like much of an athlete.

Inside, he sauntered around swinging his cane and singing loudly "I'm a rambler I'm a gambler I'm a long way from home," and other such tunes, until he came across a wealthy retired athlete who wanted to talk.

"Things aren't what they used to be," said the Devil, gesturing with his gold-headed cane.

This won over the athlete immediately, for it was just what he always said himself. He sighed sorrowfully in the direction of a portrait of J. P. Morgan and said, "No . . . things aren't like they were in the good old days. Oh, how I long for the times when men were free—free to amass a fortune, free from government interference, and free from labor unions. I often wish we could go back to them again, but I suppose it's impossible now."

"Thunderation, my good fellow, that's where you're wrong!" said the Devil, banging his cane like an old Empire Builder. "If a few responsible people like ourselves got together, we could bring back the golden age, and halt this vicious inflationary spiral. We could smash the unions and balance the budget!"

By this time many other athletes were gathering around and catching the enthusiasm in the Devil's voice. "Rout the egg-heads!" they cried, "Halt the Giveaway!" And one very old athlete in an over-stuffed chair kept shouting something about Free Silver.

So under the Devil's influence they formed a "Turn Back the Clock" movement to do away with the unions and to keep the government out of business. In order to indicate the youthful spirit that pervaded all this they decided to call themselves the Freedom Fighters.

Fortunately for the Devil's purposes at this time, the unions had all but destroyed themselves with corruption, and were run in many places by racketeers. "We will declare war on the unions," the Devil announced. A lot of people thought he was speaking in a figurative sense, but really he was speaking quite literally. With his help, the companies represented by the Freedom Fighters built up factory arsenals with machine guns and recoil-less rifles, to equip the new factory police forces, until these forces became every bit as good as some of the finest small armies in the world, capable of rushing rapidly to trouble spots and "putting out fires," so to speak, in labor-management relations.

Of course the unions put up a strong fight, but weakened as they were by corruption and scandals they capitulated; soon there were no more unions, and the Freedom Fighters had won their first great victory.

This enabled the Freedom Fighters to put their theory about halting inflation to work. They lowered wages quite a bit, and prices remained stationary. Then they lowered wages some more (and increased profits just a little to stimulate enterprise) but prices still didn't come down. The next time they lowered wages, prices actually went up, and kept on going up. But by this time everyone had forgotten about the theory.

So the wages of the workers kept going lower and lower, while the work day they put in became longer and longer. The 8-hour day was replaced by the 10-hour day, for the Supreme Court threw out the old law limiting the hours. The Court referred to it as "an unwarrantable interference with the right of both the employer and the employee in making contracts." The 5-day week gave way to the 6-day week, so that the workers could make more money—that is, as much as they were making before the movement started, almost. The same thing later caused the 12-hour day to come in, with the 7-day week, for it was found that some of the workers were not making enough to eat.

But even at that the economy was felt to require the addition of women and children to the work force. The laws against child labor were repealed, allowing children to work alongside their parents in the mills. Later child labor became compulsory from the age of eight on up.

Certain congenital gripers and trouble makers made it their business to go around investigating conditions. They found, for instance, that in some places children worked all night, with cold water being thrown in their faces to keep them from falling asleep. In one area little girls worked sixteen hours a day at the canning factories. And 10-year-old "breaker boys" in the mines crouched over coal chutes to pick slate from the coal as it passed by for ten hours a day.

But there are always complainers against every movement, and so these findings were ignored by the Freedom Fighters, as was the claim that, with the disappearance of worker safety laws, up to 500,000 workers were killed or maimed in factory accidents annually under the new set-up.

Instead, the arch-conservatives concentrated their attention on building up their Anti-Strike Association, for even without the unions, there were sporadic attempts to strike. They had legislation passed making it illegal for workers to picket plants, and arranged to have the police come in and arrest anyone who dared to violate this law.

After taking care of these things, the next goal was to get the government out of business. "Government interference is the only force now upsetting the delicate laws of the market place," said Lucifer, still swinging his gold cane, "It must be removed." So the federal regulatory agencies, like the unions, disappeared.

Life began to resemble the 1890's. The trusts were in the news again, and there was much agitation to get rid of anti-trust legislation. There was no point in going half way, Lucifer said. "If you are going to re-create really free enterprise and establish once again the laws of supply and demand in their God-given place," he explained, "you have to turn the clock back all the way, and not just a few minutes."

So anti-trust legislation went too, and by and by many big combines and interlocking corporations formed, and every day the papers told of mergers and more mergers, until each line of industry was represented by only one company, which generally would advertise that it was able to give such good public service precisely because it was so big, and because it was the only company in the business. But some companies no longer bothered with advertising; they said it was a waste of money, because where else would the people go anyway—they were the only place you could get their product.

One company owned all the oil there was, one company made all the automobiles, one company had the market cornered on food, and so forth. And for a while they all gave excellent service. But then for some reason prices started to rise again, and they kept going, higher than ever before, higher in fact than anyone had ever thought possible, and this was accompanied by a recession.

Then suddenly there was a change in the policies of the Freedom Fighters. Some of the more advanced thinkers among them criticized the government for standing idly by and not doing anything to help business. As hard times came on, they wanted the government to *do something* about the economic situation, although a short time before they said all they wanted from the government was to be left alone.

As a concrete suggestion, the Devil thought it would be wise if the Senate would be returned to what it was earlier in history, namely a body of men appointed, rather than elected directly by the people. Later on this was extended successfully to other parts of the government, in an effort to find a solution to the depression, so that to become eligible for high public office a man had to show possessions valuing at least a million dollars. Most of the old athletes from the club were well qualified for this.

Some of these wealthy men thought that excessive

government spending was responsible for the depression, and they looked around for ways to cut it down. One of the first things to go was Social Security; they said it induced a false sense of belonging in too many people. Before a Senate Committee on the matter, one wealthy magnate testified, "You cannot wet-nurse people from the time they are born until the time they die. They have got to wade in and get stuck, and that is the way men are educated and cultivated." Others said that Social Security was turning the country into nothing but a Welfare State and a Communist Collective, and that it had to go, along with all the other Socialistic Schemes that had been put in over the years.

One of the things apparently classified as a socialistic scheme was public education; at any rate it went out of style. All the children ever learned was communism anyway, most of the Freedom Fighters felt. Knowledge among the peasants meant nothing but trouble; it made them dissatisfied with staying in their place. It would be much better to restrict knowledge to the upper and more responsible classes, where it could do no harm.

After the unions disappeared, and the Income Tax was repealed, and the child labor laws forgotten, things still did not seem quite right to the Freedom Fighters. There was still too much waste, the laboring man was still "running away with the lion's share" as they said, so that it was almost impossible for an honest and enterprising individual to make a living, and to make a go of something he had sunk his life's work into. Worst of all, the enterprising man wasn't sufficiently assured of getting a return on his investment.

Something still had to be done. There was too much

irresponsible spending among the masses. Although each worker and his family did not earn very much, still, the arch-conservatives said, none of the wage earners appreciated the value of money. They didn't know how to spend their wages, and when everyone collectively spent foolishly there was nothing but mob psychology and panic in the market place. The wage-earner, they said, was nothing but a victim of the communists, and thus became a dagger at the throat of those who did know how to use money.

The wage-earner must go, they said. So the big businesses, instead of paying wages any more decided to provide for the reasonable needs and wants of the workers in exchange for the day's work. This had the added advantage of stabilizing the labor force—for very few workers, seeing that they were now without funds and completely dependent upon their company for support, felt free to seek new jobs. The only way that workers switched jobs under the new paternal system was when one company would "sell" laborers to another.

A few die-hards said that this was nothing but slavery, which the human race had so long worked to throw off, but they were dismissed as cranks and woolly-headed liberals. It was strange, though, how the worker-markets that sprang up resembled the slave-markets of old.

In fact after a few decades of this everyone found himself referring to them as "slave markets," and to the system as slavery, and the arch-conservatives generally adopted the attitude of "Well, what of it?" contending that whatever it was, it was certainly better than fighting the unions.

In this time it was very difficult to think straight. For example some businessmen refused to go along with the new system, saying that the human race was throwing away hard won gains, and that in the final reckoning business itself would suffer. And even some men of God got confused somehow into thinking that their allegiance was to a special class, to the influential, and to the return of a bygone age. They spent their time preaching to the poor, telling them that they ought to give up whatever was demanded of them, and to do it cheerfully.

Now in one state there was a great river. At first its banks were desolate and no one wanted to go near there, it was so wild. But then the government, long before the Freedom Fighters came, built a series of huge dams, bringing heat and light and power to the area, so that cities and towns sprang up where there was nothing, and schools and everything of culture, until it was the finest place in the nation to live.

Then a newcomer moved into the area and set up a small shop, outside of which he put the sign Private Power Inc. Almost immediately he started printing letters to the public in the newspaper, demanding that the government get out of the power business. He said that it was wrong for the government to compete with private power, and that what it was was creeping socialism.

People asked him what his solution would be, and he said that the government ought to sell out to private power.

He took his case to the government, and the new Senate said yes, the government certainly had no right to be competing with business. "Let us sell the whole socialistic venture to some private company," they said. "What is the nearest power company to the area?"

"My own company, Private Power Inc., is right in the middle of the valley," replied the businessman.

And they said, "Fine, we will sell it to you for $1.00, provided you keep your eye open for forest fires."

So the man went back home the proud owner of the whole system, and of practically everything else in the valley, and after that he was known as a "businessman's businessman," and his opinions were always consulted on the best ways to fight communism.

One especially happy by-product of the arch-conservative revolution was that it certainly made the railroads healthy again. The government returned to its policy of giving away public lands to the railroads in the hopes that they would open up the nation. The railroads took the land grants, but the nation had already largely been opened up, so service did not noticeably improve.

Public parks disappeared pretty fast, too. Some made choice residential sites and others were cut up for factories; what was left became hunting grounds for the very wealthy, and the sound of the fox chase was once again heard in the land.

But then in their finest hour, the Freedom Fighters did not get along. The Devil left to look into some diamond mines in South Africa, and after he was gone there were disputes among factions and groups, and squabbling for governmental power, in some cases even involving killing and poisoning, until people said that the world had not seen such things since the days of the Borgias. Soon there were only two factions left, and they struggled between themselves for control of the government. By strange coincidence one was led by a man named Hapsburg, and the other by a man named Bourbon. In an effort to stabilize things the Hapsburgs were finally persuaded by the Bourbons to get out of government entirely, and to take up dairy farming.

With the beginning of Bourbon ascendency, the very wealthy took on strange ways. Each one claimed to have royal blood in his veins, and the number one Bourbon openly called himself "King." One noble called himself a Maharajah, and held great spectacles with elephants parading and so forth. Another said he was a feudal baron, and built himself a castle, from which he used to emerge from time to time to prey on commerce. Another styled himself after Ivan the Terrible, and did what he could to live up to his name.

But with all this, business did not really go so well. With the disappearance of the consumer the companies fell to pieces. The serfs kept pretty much to themselves, and you couldn't get the food they raised away from them, even with the help of the King's mercenaries.

After that things fell apart awfully fast. There was a short time during which things resembled the glory of ancient Rome, and an evanescent Greek period when the few remaining noblemen talked philosophy and remodelled their homes with Corinthian columns, and put holes in the roof over their living rooms. Then the Bronze Age made a brief appearance, until the skill of handling that metal was lost, too, and at last humanity knew it had reached the end of the trail: the Stone Age, the oldest and most conservative of them all.

Everybody was discontented—the common people

EQUALITY FOR WE FEW
DOWN WITH WOOLY LIBERALS & MASTODONS
ANTI-COMMIE
CONSERVAT
CAVE

because they had lost everything, and the arch-conservatives because there were no more Good Old Days to go back to. They tried for a while to corner the market on arrowheads, but there was too much stone around and it was hopeless. So the Conservatives got mad at everybody else, and denounced things in general as a communist plot, and turned, and disappeared into the darkness of their caves, and they were never heard from again, leaving the rest of mankind to find the way back to civilization by themselves.

how to found your own religion

It took people a long time to get over the events related in the last chapter. When they did, it happened that a "how-to-do-it" movement was sweeping the earth. Needless to say, there was much discussion among the devils in hell about the best way of making it go to work for them. A lot of ideas were suggested. A "how-to-sin" movement was rejected as being rather unnecessary; and a "do-it-yourself" course on going to hell sounded too ridiculous to be taken seriously. But when one exceptionally sharp devil said that it would be a fine thing if they could start a "how-to-found-your-own-religion" movement, Lucifer knew that it was what they were after.

"Yes yes yes!" he cried, and closed his eyes to think. Then, his eyes still closed, and looking somewhat like a fashion designer in the throes of creation, he said, "I see it as a correspondence course . . . with myself as the director . . . we'll go after the people who are always sending away for things . . . of course . . ." Then, coming out of his trance, he said in a very business-like manner, "Why didn't we think of this sooner? We must get to work. First, we'll need a name."

It was not even two weeks later that the first full-page advertisements started to appear in the magazines. WHY NOT FOUND YOUR OWN RELIGION? they asked, in big black type. The smiling face of a man called "Dr. Golightly" looked out at you as you read this, and under his picture it said that he was the director of the famed "Golightly Correspondence Courses" that had brought home education to so many. It also said that he had founded eight different religions himself, although at present he did not belong to any of them, as he was too busy thinking up number nine.

Down the page the ad continued: "Don't be a wallflower all your life—Go out and found your own religion!"

Next there were two testimonial letters as to the efficacy of the Golightly Correspondence Course. One woman wrote:

> Before taking up with DR. GOLIGHTLY, I was just another wallflower. I could neither dance, nor converse, nor play a musical instrument. Then some kind soul placed in my hand a copy of HOW TO FOUND YOUR OWN RELIGION, Dr. Golightly's powerful booklet available to all for only 65¢. That was the greatest investment I have ever made. Immediately my life changed. I went out and started my own church, giving myself a prominent position therein, and now I have dozens of followers.
>
> I cannot recommend Dr. Golightly's book too highly. I can truthfully say that if it were not for Dr. Golightly's book, *I would not be a prophet today.*

Another testimonial said:

> Until I enrolled in DR. GOLIGHTLY's correspondence course on HOW TO FOUND YOUR OWN RELIGION, I was just another drab human being, leading a life of boredom. Nothing ever happened. Now, 6 months later, I see visions, dream dreams, call up spirits, levitate, and perform Divine Metaphysical Research. Truly,

that 65¢ was the best money I ever invested. Through my powers of prophecy alone I have cashed in on the stock market innumerable times, amazing my less divine friends.

I am now planning a temple to myself, to be constructed entirely out of topaz, at great cost. Like the great cathedrals of the middle ages, it will take centuries to complete. I cannot praise this course too highly.

At this point, some space was given to handling possible objections. The advertisement stated in a frank and friendly manner:

WE FIND THERE ARE 3 COMMON OBJECTIONS THAT PEOPLE MAKE WHEN WE SAY "FOUND YOUR OWN RELIGION." THEY ARE ALL QUITE EASILY DISMISSED—

Objection #1—"I haven't got the time."

Make time, we answer! Add up all the minutes you waste every day and see what they amount to. If you can then conscientiously come to us and say you haven't got the time, we will believe you. But remember—all you need is *15 minutes* a day! Give us just 15 minutes a day, and in 3 weeks we'll have you running your own religion. We guarantee this.

Objection #2—"But I've already got *a religion."*

We have utterly no use for people who hide behind such statements. If you want to go around with a second-hand religion all your life, if you are willing to live your whole life letting someone else call the shots, that's your funeral, not ours. But you'd be much better off coming along with us.

Objection #3—"Who am I to found a religion? I'm not good enough to do anything like that."

False pride. Hypocritical, pharisaical pride. Deep down inside you, you know very well that you could preach a better sermon than the one you hear each

> Sunday morning. Now honestly, couldn't you? Besides, even if you do feel shy, it's only natural to experience a little modest hesitation in something like this before you plunge in. But the important thing is to plunge! Do your share! The whole world is waiting for your message.

With such high-powered copy, it is not surprising that the Golightly course received pounds and pounds of applications from people everywhere. Some merely wanted to take enough lessons to be prophets. Others, more farsighted, wanted explicit instructions on how to silence critics and make converts. And there were a few who wanted the blueprints for a temple of topaz, so that they might be enshrined in honor for all the ages.

The devils were all ready for them. Correspondence lesson number one in the Golightly series was called HOW TO GET STARTED.

It listed the seven most popular ways of starting your own religion. It said for example that in the past, one of the most popular methods was to go out in your back yard and dig up some stone tablets containing clear and unmistakable references to you, and giving you a mandate to start an exceptionally fine religion immediately. However, the only way that you can dig up stone tablets that refer to you, practically speaking, is to bury them yourself, first. The whole thing is an awkward process, the Golightly course felt, and one fraught with danger to the inexperienced. Even in such a matter as the wording of the inscription, extreme caution had to be observed, as the stone tablets were likely to come in for close scrutiny later on as the grand charter of your whole movement. Any sloppy spelling or unclear modifiers, and you might find yourself in some very tight spots afterwards; you might even be maneuvered out of the role of Founding Father eventually by some of your more legal-minded followers.

So many hazards were involved in the method that a safe sample form for a suitable stone tablet (or papyrus) was included in the first lesson. "Make sure that you remain a Founding Father," it said. "Keep to the formula."

There were, however, many other less difficult methods. While they did not possess the strong impact of the stone tablet technique, they were, nevertheless, not to be underrated. Powerful personalities, the lesson said, might find that a simple, dogmatic statement of one's supernatural prerogatives is the best technique of all. "For simplicity," said the lesson, "nothing can beat the direct approach.

> Walk up to a prospective convert, stare at him for 3 minutes (without blinking) and state clearly and distinctly whatever you consider to be the most fundamental tenet of the religion you are trying to create. Most of all, *believe it yourself;* if the nature of the matter renders this impossible, then at least take voice lessons. But always remember: if you can convince yourself, you cannot fail to convince others. Once you have convinced yourself that the new doctrines are real, the hardest part is over. You have won your first convert.

As the direct-approach method outlined above was likely to be a bit hard on people with sensitive temperaments or weak hearts, the lesson went on to give a long list of tried and true methods meant for the person of only average talent. It mentioned some of the more obvious methods available, such as spreading rumors that you are a holy person, or confiding modestly to friends that you are regularly favored with mystical experiences. Then it went on to say: "Examine closely the churches in your town for any niches unoccupied by statues. If you find one, stand in it and see if you attract any devotion—perhaps you have an honest face. It's not much, but it's a beginning, and people have started religions with less."

One other thing in this first lesson gave some indication of the great enterprise of those behind the Golightly course: an ad for a Junior Course in Religion Founding for boys and girls in the 8 to 12 age bracket. "Have your children found their own religion, too," the ad told parents. "Contrary to popular opinion, many children are actually better at religion-founding than adults." And then addressing itself to the children, the ad said, "Boys and Girls, it's fun to found your own religion—be the first kid on your block to do it!"

Lesson Number 2 was entitled, "Should God Have Any Place in Your Religion?"

The answers to this question were purely exploratory; the lesson said that it did not want to persuade founders one way or the other. Instead it contented itself with pointing out the various strengths and weaknesses of possible solutions. Leaving God in, the lesson stated, on the one hand (it could not be denied) carried with it a certain atmosphere of traditionalism and legitimacy, which would unquestionably lend your new religion a sense of dignity—something which the new religion needs as quickly as it can get it. On the other hand, the course continued, keeping God in does unquestionably leave the religion-founder "playing second fiddle," as the popular phrase has it.

You could tell that, though he wasn't saying it, Dr. Golightly favored a compromise. There would come times, he counseled, in which you would prefer to have God in your religion, other times in which you would not. A certain extremely vague hint that God is involved somewhere, and that you are thus not running things entirely by yourself, would have the advantage that, when needed, He could be brought in, but otherwise left in the background.

From this the lesson went on to the question of Jesus Christ. It noted that if the problem of God was a difficult one for the amateur, the difficulties were generally compounded with the introduction of Christ. "Will Jesus Christ have any place in your church?" the lesson asked.

> If so, decide now precisely what that place is to be, as this is apt to be a most complicating development. Once you accept Christ, you find yourself forced to let in a whole train of doctrines and practices from the world of a bygone day, some of which may turn out to be extremely repugnant to you. "If I had it to do over," says one of our most successful religion founders, who has founded no less than 36 completely new and different faiths, "I would keep Christ out of religion. For in this connection, what first appears as a source of justification for the hard-pressed religion-founder quickly becomes a strait-jacket, hindering all sense of experiment; the discovery that a certain Christ-like attitude and behavior will naturally be expected of you at every moment of the day can come as a decidedly unpleasant surprise to the religion founder who has not thought of it. No, the older I get at this business of founding new religions, the more I say: Keep Christ out of it."

> We heartily share in the old veteran's concern; we suggest relegating Christ to the world of art and literature. An excellent solution is to admit that He was the world's greatest poet, and be done with it.

You could tell that the next lesson was intended as a sort of breather. It went back for a while to one of the original problems that might still be bothering the student: Lesson Number 3—"Is There Any Limit to the Number of New Religions That Will Be Founded?"

> Experts estimate that there are in the world at the present time over 400 different religious sects. Needless to say, that number will need considerable revision once the Golightly course becomes popular. It is our considered opinion that there is room for many times that number—the only absolute limit being the total number of individuals there are in the world at a given time.
>
> However, if you grant it possible that one individual can hold two or more religions simultaneously, then we see that the horizon is greatly broadened, and the future of religion-founding is shown to be a very bright one indeed.
>
> In this connection, it is interesting to theorize about what will then take place in the world of church architecture. As the do-it-yourself movement in religion proceeds to its obvious and final completion, i.e., each church consisting of a single human being, the size of the average church building is bound to grow smaller and smaller, while the number of church buildings conversely grows larger and larger. When the terminus of the process is at last reached, it is reasonable to expect that the normal church will at that time be no larger than a phone booth, which indeed it will resemble in many ways, being however more highly ornate. Happily, there should be great numbers of them everywhere visible.

IGLESIA
CHA-CHA-CHA-
SI
DIOS.....NO
MY
KINGDOM
CAME
+ + +
TEMPLE
OF THE
SPLIT-LEVEL
GOSPEL
1ST
CHURCH
OF THE
MELLOW
FELLOWSHIP

BE DEMOCRATIC, shouted the next lesson, Number 4, before Number 3's startling prophecies could really be digested:

> In all truly modern religions, everything is decided by Majority Rule. All doctrines, even such fundamental ones as whether we can find salvation or not, must be submitted to a vote every so often, for the modern parish is nothing if not changing. You will be amazed how doctrines come and go—how at one time your congregation will vote in Grace by a landslide, while at another they will vote it out of existence.
>
> However, for the sake of Peace of Mind, you had better be prepared to do a little lobbying.
>
> Of course, Majority Rule has its difficulties. Tired husbands will complain that they cannot make it to all the meetings, and that the housewives in their absence keep voting the existence of God in and out, in typical womanly fashion. How can it be, the men will ask you, that God's existence can depend on the wishes of half a dozen housewives who never miss a vote? (Recognize such questioning at once as morbid, and do not hesitate to recommend the psychiatrist's office.)
>
> Such difficulties may naturally occur to you, too. In order to keep yourself from becoming too involved, it is suggested that you believe and practice a religion different from that of your parishioners.

HAVE YOU THOUGHT OF A CREDO? asked the next lesson, lesson Number 5:

> Students cannot expect the course to supply them with a ready-made Credo; it would not be fair to them, for there would then be duplication—one person would end up believing the same as the next, and there would be no variety whatever.
>
> We can, however, show what has been done in the past. Here is a sample Credo, written by a student after taking only three lessons:

CREDO
by Audrey Semple Packerson

I feel more or less that there is One God.
I also like to believe that He created Heaven and Earth, although this is not of course necessary.
I like to think that He became Man; quite possibly He died for our sins.
Whether He was buried or not is for someone else to decide.
For those who can see their way clear to believing, it is nice also to think that He rose from the dead.
But most of all, it is in Myself that I believe.
Amen.

"Could you do any better?" Dr. Golightly asked.

The lessons went on and on. The title of the next one was, "How To Become A Myth." The one after that supplied students with a simplified version of the 10 Commandments which really consisted in only five, an economy made possible by dropping such things as Adultery, Theft and Murder from the area of morality. One fascinating lesson was meant for those who did not think themselves clever enough to think up a religion. It was called "100 Beautiful Ideas In Search of A Religion." Another went into the thorny problem of the Liturgy—"Ritual: With It Or Without It?" For those who were in favor of it, the course stressed a liturgy based on the wonders of modern science, and a liturgical year with a cycle of feasts in honor of great scientific discoveries. Christmas, for instance, was to be replaced by a feast in honor of Boyle's Law. "Modern science," the lesson stated, "has come to supply man with all the ritual he needs, a ritual decidedly apocalyptic and eschatological in character, looking forward as it does so intently to the Last Things, especially to that Great Fusion Day when all will be One."

By the time the last lesson in the course had been stamped and put in the mail, the devils were having so much fun that they just couldn't let the campaign die. They too were bitten by the How-To movement, and they rushed out to start their own religions. Most of them turned out to be very capable at this, as centuries of experience with black magic and occult practices had given them a certain feel for it.

Truly the earth had never seen such a revival of interest in religion; the devils had not enjoyed themselves so much since the good old days just before the Flood. They competed with one another in devilishness, and even fought with one another in their excitement.

All in all, it looked like just about the greatest thing the devils had ever pulled. False prophets, Witch Doctors and Medicine Men abounded in pulpits throughout the land; in some cases the devils quite openly mounted the pulpits with no attempt to conceal their identity.

In short, the whole process was well on the way to certain well-known excesses usually identified with the time when Moloch reigned on earth. To the devils, carried away with themselves, it seemed almost too good to be true.

Then right in the middle of everything the trumpet sounded, and they were all called back to hell. At the first blast they all went tumbling out of their new pulpits, in the midst of sermons even, and they went hurtling over and over and down and down, deep into the abyss, where they knew Lucifer himself would be waiting for them.

The meeting was a little while getting started, but Lucifer waited for them all to arrive and be seated. Some were trying to find their places, while others were still divesting themselves of surplices, stoles, prayer shawls and other regalia. Through it all the stately figure in front of them patiently waited. When there was complete silence, and everyone was straining forward to hear what it was he had to tell them, Lucifer finally spoke.

"In the Beginning," he stated grandly, "God created Heaven and Earth," and a great moan of protest rose from their endless ranks: it was to be another of his catechism lessons, for which he was among them justly famous, and which he held from time to time whenever he felt that they were all beginning to miss the point of things. Sometimes these were more like retreat conferences, and then Lucifer would be available afterward for consultation and spiritual direction. At other times they were of a strictly academic nature, for the Devil loved nothing more than to deliver a learned paper on some tract of Moral or Dogmatic Theology.

This particular talk was pretty much a one-man *disputatio*, full of *sed contra*'s, *strictiore sensu*'s and *doctores scinduntur*'s. So stimulating was his line of thought that the other Devils lost their sense of pique at being called back, and followed his argument with a very keen delight. After starting with a series of profound observations on Habitual Grace he moved on to explore the nature of the character imprinted by some of the sacraments, and finally worked around to the subject of whether Extreme Unction was one of the sacraments which enjoyed reviviscence or not. (He held with the majority of theologians that it did.)

For whatever he said, the Devil was careful to have authorities. He cautiously distinguished for them between what was *De Fide Divina et Catholica* and what was merely *sententia communis.* He spoke often of Cajetan, John of Saint Thomas, and the Greek Fathers; and he quoted the *Summa Theologiae* a lot. "But what does Thomas say, what is said of this matter by Aquinas?" he would shrilly shout, and you could hear the question ". . . Aquinas? . . . Aquinas? . . . Aquinas?" echo back and forth, up and down, all through the caverns of Hell.

Altogether the whole thing was a remarkable piece of scholarly presentation. Above all, it was dispassionate, except for a brief interval where he took issue with certain *dicta* of Cardinal Billot and the Jesuits, who, he clearly felt, were inclined to be rather loose on some things, and anything but reliable guides to the inquiring mind.

Through all this, he made no mention of their recent successes among the Sons of Men. He refrained entirely from any mention of it, neither praising them nor blaming them for the confusions they had sowed upon earth. He treated the whole matter plainly as being somewhat beside the point, and of little relevance to his lecture.

After it was all over, he zipped up his briefcase and left them—but not before he had assigned them a terrible amount of homework. Then pensively he retired to his quarters, and all Hell sat down to review its theology.

the devil as hidden persuader

At that time there was a great Public Relations man who was so clever he could convince anybody of anything, and he could make anybody buy anything. He was so persuasive and so successful that there really weren't any challenges left for him, and he was very sad.

Every night in his sumptuous apartment he used to weep over the fact that there were no more worlds for him to conquer. "All the really impossible things have already been pulled," he would say, his tears streaming down into his drink.

One night he was in a deeper depression than usual, and he cursed his luck, that he should be born with the ability to sell the Devil himself, but that the world would never learn of it. Suddenly the Devil appeared before him. "How about being my Public Relations man?" asked the Devil. "I need one very badly. Everyone else has one but me, and I am falling behind. The Government has them, the Church has them, and even the gangsters have them. No one has any time left to be tempted anymore—they are all too busy reading publicity releases. In fact, I don't have too much time to spend tempting them, I have to spend so much catching up on releases myself. Only your skill can help me out of this predicament. Will you take me on?"

The great PR man was overjoyed; of course he would take the Devil on as his client. At last he had a chance to show his stuff: anyone who could sell the Devil would surely go down as the greatest salesman in history.

The first thing the PR man did was to set up a national headquarters for the Devil in New York, with branch offices in Hollywood and Chicago. He decided after much thinking that it was going to have to be a hard-sell job, with no shilly-shallying about who his client was. In this type of case the American people would appreciate frankness, he felt, and would like to know where they stood. So he put the Devil's name on the door and a heavy carpet on the floor and waited for the newsmen.

Meantime, he got other PR men to handle things. News of the multi-million dollar account did not take long to spread through the world of PR, and soon the best in the business were available, happy to sell their talents to the Devil. The networks began shifting programs around to leave openings for some of the many millions, and the magazines and newspapers prepared to have pages of extra space that could be utilized at a moment's notice.

The great PR man decided that they should start things off with a brainstorming session for the ad men. Coffee and doughnuts were served in his apartment to them, and secretaries waited to take down suggestions. On a blackboard in front of the gathering was written the question, in huge letters, HOW SELL DEVIL TO PUBLIC?

"Give him an eye-patch!" shouted the first ad man to think of a solution, and the secretaries took it down.

"Make him a Father Image," said one persuader hidden in the crowd.

"Use spot announcements," mumbled an unenthusiastic voice, while an excited one added, "Use animated cartoons!"

One little ad man apparently was greatly convinced of the power of the color red. He started off by saying, confusingly, that he thought they should use red packages. Then after that, whenever anybody else mentioned anything, he would add, "And put it in red," or "Use red lettering."

"Make him look like Liberace," came from the back of the room, and someone else said, "Get him an Oscar."

At this point the great PR man himself stepped forward. He held up his hand and said, "Later. That stuff is good for later on. But let's face it: we've got a criminal on our hands. A real desperado. He's responsible for every crime in the books—different people think of him as different things. Mothers think of him as a kidnapper. Bankers think of him as an embezzler. Used car dealers think of him as another used car dealer.

"We can't start off by asking them to take this crook into their *homes*. No. First we got to make him the underdog. We got to say he has no friends, no place to go, that he ain't even got a job. Americans are suckers for the down and outer, and that's just what we're going to make our client for the first part of the campaign."

The job of making the Devil an underdog proved much simpler than anybody expected, for as soon as the news of the Devil's arrival at Idlewild reached Washington, three different Congressional committees wanted to have him subpoenaed, to explain his presence on these fair shores. A special sub-committee on vigilance won out and served the subpoena, and became the first Congressional body in history to have the Devil appear before it. There was a lot of speculation about whether the Devil would take the Fifth Amendment; as it turned out, he didn't.

The hearing was to be televised, and the entire nation was interested in seeing what the Devil looked like. So the PR men had a group of make-up experts come and make him look presentable. They made him wear a blue shirt, and glasses, which he was supposed to take off and put on every once in a while as he answered questions. It was the glasses that did wonders for him, as somehow no one expected the Devil to be wearing glasses. When his picture first flashed across the screen 35 million housewives said almost in unison, "He doesn't look at all as bad as I thought he would."

The scriptwriters in charge of his defense had a large number of lawyers at their disposal. They also had a large variety of different scripts to choose from, depending on which way the hearings went, and what the plot called for. And they had prepared statements, which they passed out by the armful every hour to waiting newsmen.

The first of these pointed out that the Devil had no mother. It was done on the advice of an old politician who said he had won eleven different elections by campaigning simply and solely on the plea that he had no mother (which, as a matter of fact, he did have) and he said that if it worked for him he didn't see why it

PROJECT
!!!

shouldn't work for the Devil. It was an outstanding success; there was no way of telling how much of the orphan vote it brought in, but it was obvious that it pulled at the heart of almost anyone.

The next release told of how the Devil planned to "go straight." It spoke of how he knew that this was his "big chance" to go right, that he knew an awful lot of people were pulling for him and trying to help him, and that he certainly wasn't going to let these people down. "Everyone deserves a chance," said the news reports, "and this week the Devil will get his."

Another told of how he helped a little boy get his dog back from the dog pound, and others included accounts of his giving to the Heart Fund, giving advice to juvenile delinquents (*good* advice), speaking to a farmer over the fence about his hay crop, and so forth.

Then the pictures started to come. They showed the Devil giving up strong drink, refusing to buy bad magazines, helping an officer of the law, and helping a little old lady across the street. And there were others, such as an unending series of poses with beauty queens from every state in the nation.

He was, needless to say, greatly appreciated by newsmen, who enjoyed having such a sure-fire subject, and so it was not surprising when it turned out that the Devil actually enjoyed a good press. The reporters hauled out their folksiest styles for the people back home. Wrote one:

> WASHINGTON—Lucifer K. Beelzebub rolled into town today and gave this sleepy city on the Potomac something to wake up and talk about. Looking a far cry from the wicked Old Nick you hear about when you're a child, he sang "America the Beautiful" for

> reporters on the Capitol lawn, and followed it up with "Barbara Fritchie," without a single mistake.
>
> Whisked by Secret Servicemen on a rapid tour of the city's shrines, he never failed to be visibly moved by anything he was presented with. He wept at the Washington Monument, he wept at the Lincoln Memorial, and (due to a mistake) he even wept in front of Hogate's, a famous restaurant where they sell fish.
>
> Shown several of the city's great churches, the Devil said that although he did not see eye to eye with those who built such structures, still, he had a healthy respect for what was behind all that, and only wished that it were possible for him to co-operate more closely with such people, but that it was too bad, that he simply could not see his way clear to doing this.

As a matter of fact, on the occasion just referred to, the Devil had been about to go into a long disquisition upon Toleration, which was one of his favorite topics, and upon which he held most energetic views, when one of the aides who were with him clapped a hand over his client's mouth and said jokingly that such matters had best be left for the preachers and judges. Everyone laughed, but the PR men learned their lesson that day, and decided to keep the Devil's personal comments to a minimum.

The hearings came to an indecisive conclusion; that is, legally they were indecisive. In every other way they were a great success for the Devil.

The Devil himself never again had to say anything, nor show up for anything. For all practical purposes he could have gone back to Hell, for the PR men were far better able than he was to say what he should say on every important occasion. Press releases written in

July were ready long before their Christmas deadline; his responses to attacks were masterpieces of clear thinking and dignified rebuttal. The Devil (that is, his PR men) had something to say about everything: train wrecks, the price of living, favorite movie stars, the best seller lists and so on.

The national picture magazines had the Devil's face all over them, looking out at America. Some had him posed in a thoughtful mood, holding a cigarette as its wisps of smoke curled around a neat little tattoo on his hand. One went "yachting with the Devil" and showed him leaning far out on the high side of a racing sail boat. The Devil was an "old car enthusiast," readers were told by another. It showed him bouncing along the highway in a 1928 Studebaker.

Of course, the Devil was required to tell the story of his life. He got $37,000 for it in one of those "as-told-to" arrangements. From his way of telling it, Hell was just another old home town sort of place, and even talking about it made him homesick for the neighborhood of his early days. He would have been a "right guy" except that someone had given him a "bum steer" a long time ago and he was still paying for it. He was very reluctant to go along with his ghost writers on the ending, but they finally won out and so he ended by telling all kids everywhere to stay off the streets.

Then one day the ad men woke up to find the Devil had gone home. Some thought that he had been frightened off by some of the things they had planned for him—one group had prepared a song for him to sing with a guitar, and others were saying that they saw no reason why the drive should stop short of the presidency for their client. But they should have known that the Devil was really the oldest hidden persuader of them all, and had good reasons for remaining hidden.

The Devil had gone back to Hell because he didn't see that he was needed up on earth anymore. The PR men were doing as good a job as he could do: it was plain that the image-makers didn't need him, all they needed was his image. The Devil saw that he was only in the way. So he went back to Hell, where he was sorely needed, confident that his affairs were in good hands.

The Devil left a note explaining all this to the great PR man, who in turn told the ad men that everything was going to be all right. The Devil would keep them supplied from below with all the necessary support for years to come. This seemed to satisfy everybody, even the song-writers who had written the special number for the Devil; they figured that they could get it into the top 40 even without him.

But no one was happier than the great PR man himself. There were tears in his eyes and he found it hard to swallow each time he read the way the note referred to him. It began, "To the greatest PR man in the whole wide world," and it was signed, "—from one who certainly ought to know."